HENRY FIELDING

TOM JONES

By the Same Author :

1.	Henry Fielding	:	**Joseph Andrews**
2.	Henry Fielding	:	**Tom Jones**
3.	D.H. Lawrence	:	**Sons and Lovers**
4.	D.H. Lawrence	:	**The Rainbow**
5.	Jane Austen	:	**Pride and Prejudice**
6.	Charles Dickens	:	**Oliver Twist**
7.	Charles Dickens	:	**David Copperfield**
8.	S.T. Coleridge	:	**The Rime of the Ancient Mariner**
9.	S.T. Coleridge	:	**An Evaluation of His Poetry**
10.	William Wordsworth	:	**Select Poems**
11.	William Shakespeare	:	**Macbeth**
12.	William Shakespeare	:	**The Tempest**
13.	William Shakespeare	:	**Julius Caesar**
14.	William Shakespeare	:	**Twelfth Night**
15.	William Shakespeare	:	**The Merchant of Venice**
16.	William Shakespeare	:	**The Sonnets**

HENRY FIELDING

TOM JONES

[A Critical Study]

RAJINDER PAUL, M.A.
Formerly Head,
Department of English
Hans Raj College
(University of Delhi)
Delhi

Twenty - Ninth Edition
2019

RAMA BROTHERS INDIA PVT. LTD.
EDUCATIONAL PUBLISHERS
Janak Plaza, 2021, Bank Street,
Karol Bagh, New Delhi - 110 005

Price : **Rs. 170.00**

ISBN 81-7581-024-6

First Edition : 1973
Twenty-Ninth Edition : 2019

Published by : **RAMA BROTHERS INDIA PVT. LTD.**
(Educational Publishers)
Janak Plaza, 2021, Bank Street, Karol Bagh, New Delhi - 110 005.
Phone : 28757313, 28755936
Tele-Fax : 91-11-28755936
E-Mail : ramabrothers@hotmail.com
Website : www.ramabrothers.co.in

Laser Typesetting at **DEVIKA GRAPHICS**
2125/59, Naiwala, Karol Bagh, New Delhi - 110 005.

Cover Printed at **Mudrak**, Delhi - 110 091.

Printed at **Bright Printers**, Pahari Bhojla,
Delhi - 110 006.

PREFACE TO THE TWENTY - NINTH EDITION

Encouraged by the appreciation my critical study of *Tom Jones* received from the students, I am pleased to place before them yet another, thoroughly revised and enlarged edition. Some new chapters have now been added to make this study exhaustive; some of the very latest critical material has been incorporated and some more questions set at the recent university examinations have been discussed. The bibliography has been brought up-to-date. I hope that in its present form the book will prove even more useful to the students for whom it is meant.

And now it is my pleasant duty to thank my publishers Messrs Rama Brothers for their whole-hearted co-operation at all stages of the preparation of this edition.

New Delhi
February, 2019

RAJINDER PAUL

PREFACE TO THE FIRST EDITION

Tom Jones, one of the first really great English novels, has evoked very different response in different ages. While Richardson condemned it as a profligate performance and Dr. Johnson declared it as a corrupt work, Coleridge was much impressed by the whole-someness of Fielding's morality and affirmed that 'a youngman whose heart or feelings can be injured or even his passions excited, by aught in this novel, is already thoroughly corrupt'. And while Coleridge's contention that the plot of *Tom Jones* was one of the three most perfect plots ever planned has been supported by many critics, F.R. Leavis says that the conventional talk about the perfect construction of *Tom Jones* is absurd. It is evident that though the historical significance of this novel is unquestionable, it poses many serious textual problems to the students of English literature. The present work is designed to provide the student with the various, usually highly contrasted, points of view briefly but lucidly and to help him to some dispassionate, objective evaluation of the novel. To make the book really useful, some of the very latest criticism has also been incorporated.

It was never my intention to make my discussion of the novel too scholarly or pedantic. It is primarily meant for our university students at the honours and the post-graduate level, and during the course of its preparation, never, even for a moment, was I oblivious of their personal difficulties and their needs. If my work proves useful to them, I shall consider my labour amply rewarded.

And in the end, I must seize this opportunity to express my sense of gratefulness to my publishers M/s. Rama Bros. They extended me commendable assistance and co-operation and their production values are really fine.

New Delhi **RAJINDER PAUL**
September, 1973

CONTENTS

1

Henry Fielding's Life and Works

Birth and Parentage

Henry Fielding was born on 22nd April, 1707 at sharpham Park in Somersetshire in an aristocratic family claiming its descent from the famous Hapsburgs. His father Lieutenant Edmund Fielding was one of Marlborough's generals and his mother Sarah Gould was the daughter of Sir Henry Gould, a judge of the King's bench. Henry was their eldest child. His mother died in 1718 and his father married again.

Early Life

Fielding received his early education from the family chaplain, Mr. Oliver of Montcombe' who is said to be 'better fitted for the care of swine than of children'. All that he read at this stage was the Bible and some traditional romances. Next he went to Eton, where he gained proficiency in classical languages, Greek and Latin. He had hardly left Eton when he got enamoured of Sarah, the daughter of a deceased merchant of Lyme Regis and even planned abducting her. But his plans never materialised. The girl was promptly transferred to the care of another guardian and married off. All that the frustrated youth could do was to translate a part of Juvenal's sixth Satire into verse 'as all the revenge taken by an injured lover'.

Fielding the Dramatist

After a brief stay at Leyden, where he studied Civil Law, Fielding returned to London in 1728 and threw himself recklessly into all the pleasures of London life. In those days, playwriting being the only reliable means of making a living by the pen, Fielding embarked upon a dramatic career and, except tragedy, tried his hand at every kind of dramatic composition—comedy, farce, burlesque. In a few years, he became a prolific if not a successful dramatist. The more notable among his plays are: *Love in Several Masques* (1728), *The Temple Beau* (1730), *The Tragedy of Tragedies, or The Life and Death of Tom Thumb the Great* (1730–31), *The Covent Garden Tragedy* (1732), *The Miser* (1733), *Don Quixote in England* (1734), *Pasquin* (1736) and *The Historical Register for the Year 1736* (1737).

The scurrilous references to Sir Robert Walpole, the Prime Minister and the pungent attacks on the policies of the government made by Fielding particularly in his *Pasquin* and *The Register* provoked the wrath of the authorities and in 1737 they passed the Theatrical Licensing Act by which the number of theatres was reduced and Lord Chamberlain's license was made an indispensable preliminary condition for stage production of any play.

Burlesque being the only successful line of Fielding, it became impossible for him to get any license. Hence his dramatic career was abruptly cut short.

Fielding had inherited a decaying variety of Congreve's Restoration Comedy that gave little inspiration for serious writing. In the beginning of his dramatic career, he did not have much experience of human heart. In addition, his financial insecurity often obliged him to produce slipshod work. Thus, as a dramatist, Fielding could not achieve any outstanding success. Had he continued, he might have excelled at least in that kind of drama of which we consider Ben Jonson to be the great master, but that was not to be. However, his training at the theatre proved very useful to him, for it enabled him to construct his novels on dramatic principles.

Marriage Law, 'The Champion'

In Nov. 1734, Fielding married a Salisbury beauty Miss Charlotte Cradock, the original of both Sophia and Amelia, whom he had been regularly courting for about four years. He spent some extravagant time with his wife in the countryside but was soon back to London, struggling harder than ever. In November 1737, he was admitted as a student at the Middle Temple. He assiduously applied himself to the study of law and was called to the bar, in 1740, but made little headway in this profession. Meanwhile, he had never given up his literary pursuits. In November 1739, there appeared the first number of *The Champion,* a newspaper published thrice a week and written mainly by Fielding and his friend James Ralph.

Richardson's 'Pamela'; Fielding's 'Shamela'

In November 1740, Samuel Richardson published his *Pamela or Virtue Rewarded.* The novel took the entire reading public by storm, but Fielding was annoyed at the utilitarian concept of morality that *Pamela* stood for. In this novel, an attractive servant girl successfully resists her employer's attempts to seduce her and eventually prevails upon him to marry her. Fielding felt that this concept of virtue as advocated by Richardson in his novel was far removed from the true Christian virtue. It was in fact 'a code of calculated chastity with material goods for its earthly reward'. He parodied *Pamela* in his *Shamela* revealing Richardson's chaste heroine to be no better than a common prostitute.

'Joseph Andrews', 'Jonathan Wild'

Shamela was at best a brief joke. It did not satisfy Fielding's desire to expose the moral absurdities of *Pamela.* This he undertook to do in a much longer work—*Joseph Andrews* (1742). Its hero is Pamela's brother, a remarkably handsome and equally virtuous young footman who successfully resists the advances of his lascivious employer, a rich landlady. The parody is sustained till the tenth chapter, after which the novel takes a life of its own. It is evident that Fielding by now was beginning to find his moorings as a novelist. Only a year later appeared his three volumes *of Miscellanies* which include *Journey from This World to the Next One* and *The Life of Jonathan Wild the Great.* The latter, a piece of sustained irony, examines the nature of greatness and morality.

Life by now had become pretty hard for Fielding. The best part of the next two or three years he had to devote virtually to hackwork. He was 'reputed and reported the author of half the scurrility, bawdry, treason and blasphemy which these few last years have produced'. In 1746, his wife died at Bath. This was a great shock to Fielding who had passionately loved her. However, in 1747, he married his maid Mary Daniel, who made him a good wife.

' Tom Jones'

In 1748, through the efforts of Mr. Lyttleton, Fielding's old school fellow, he was made a principal Justice of peace for Middlesex and Westminster. Two other friends of his, John, Duke of Bedford and Ralph Allen of Bath, provided him with the necessary means of livelihood and at the instance of Lyttleton, by the middle of 1746, he had begun work on *Tom Jones.* It took him nearly two years to complete this novel. It was probably completed in November 1748 and published in 1749. The new type of genre that Fielding had accidentally discovered in *Joseph Andrews* was systematically developed in *Tom Jones.*

'Amelia'

Fielding's last novel *Amelia,* a much less spirited work, appeared in 1751. It reflects its author's pre-occupation with social problems and his deep interest in his professional life.

'Journal of a Voyage to Lisbon

Fielding's health was gradually deteriorating and in 1754, he was advised to go to Lisbon. The journey was highly uncomfortable and its hazards are described at length in the *Journal of a Voyage to Lisbon.* It was in August that Fielding reached there and in October, he was no more.

Fielding the Man

An estimate of Fielding the man can be accurately made from a study of *Tom Jones, Amelia* and *The Voyage to Lisbon.* He was a youngman of enormous animal vigour with good connections and friends among the privileged classes. He was turned loose in London with a shadowy allowance and invited to make his way by his wits, so we can safely visualise what sort of a career he could have in the initial stages.

Fielding's outstanding quality, was his infinite capacity for pleasure. He treated life very casually and recklessly. His happy constitution made him forget every evil and his cousin Lady Mary Wortley Montagu was persuaded that he had 'known more happy moments than any prince on earth'. Later, when he had to act as a magistrate, he was fairly sobered down, yet he never lost his 'indomitable buoyancy of spirit'. He was very much like his friend Sir Richard Steele, to both of whom was given 'that irrepressible hopefulness, and full delight of being which forgets tomorrow in today'.

Fielding was generous to a fault. He would often forego his own satisfaction to fulfil the needs of others. After he took over as a magistrate, he kept an open table for all his friends. In addition to a rare capacity for enjoyment under all circumstances and a generosity of temper, Fielding had a certain disposition to good fellowship. His concept of virtue was a genuine feeling of benevolence and he was very critical of calculated prudence. He hated all kinds of pretensions. In fact, hypocrisy and heartlessness were the greatest vices in his eyes. He gave as much importance to one's impulses as to one's actions. Like his immortal hero Tom Jones, he had led a reckless life and had often, faltered and sinned; still he was by and large a noble personality. As a magistrate he was alert and energetic, as a husband kind and tender, as a friend loyal and hospitable, and as a writer original, vigorous and very interesting.

2
Major Novels of Fielding

1. Joseph Andrews (1742)

It was the immense popularity or Richardson's *Pamela* and the disgust at the utilitarian concept of morality advocated in it that prompted Fielding to attempt a parody of it in his first novel *Joseph Andrews.* A close parallel between the two novels is maintained till the tenth chapter of *Joseph Andrews.* After that Fielding gets absorbed in his own plot and his novel develops quite independently of *Pamela.*

The novel is divided into four books. In the beginning of Book I, we are formally introduced to the two major characters of the novel, Joseph Andrews and Parson Adams, the curate. Joseph is a footboy at the Boobys'. He is supposed to be Pamela's brother and it is Pamela's aunt-in-law, Lady Booby who has promoted him to the office of the footboy on account of his strength and pluck and good looks. He has read Pamela's letters with great admiration and is determined to be chaste like her.

Sir Thomas dies and Lady Booby takes the household, including the handsome footman, up to London. There she makes amorous advances to him. But Joseph repels them as indignantly as Pamela had earlier resisted the advances of Squire Booby. In a fit of anger, Lady Booby dismisses him and he sets out on foot for his village in the west, where his fellow-servant and sweetheart Fanny has been left behind. On the way, he is robbed and beaten by a group of robbers. Almost half-dead, he is taken to an inn kept by the Tow-wouses. Here he comes across Parson Adams.

Parson Adams was on his way to London to sell nine volumes of his sermons to a publisher. But he discovers that with his usual absent-mindedness, he has forgotten to bring his sermons with him. So he also decides to return home with Joseph. The next two books describe the incidents on the roadside; Fielding exploits various encounters of Parson Adams and Joseph Andrews to expose the vanity, hypocrisy and pretensiousness of the contemporary society. They are first joined by Mrs. Slipslop, Lady Booby's elderly handmaid, who has also cast amorous eyes on Joseph, but being unsuccessful has consoled herself by penetrating her ladyship's secret and threatening to make it public. In the meanwhile, Fanny, worried on Joseph's account, has set out to meet him in London. She falls into the hands of a ruffian who tries to ravish her, but Parson Adams intervenes in the nick of time and rescues her from this disgrace. The sight of Joseph's and Fanny's fondness for each other makes Mrs. Slipslop feel extremely jealous and she soon takes flight. The story goes swinging on from one adventure to another and characters of every complexion appear at every turn. Fanny, Joseph and Parson Adams are joined in the third book by the benevolent Mr. Wilson, who tells them the story of his misguided youth, his downfall and reformation, and his retirement to a life according to nature. Mr. Wilson's edifying history is not particularly interesting, but it is made somewhat relevant towards the end of the novel.

In Book IV, all the chief persons are brought together, as in the last act of a well-knit comedy. Lady Booby, her insulted passion for Joseph battling with her resentment, comes home again, to find Joseph and Fanny preparing for their union, under the fatherly protection of the Parson. Storming and raging, she forbids Adams to publish the banns, and failing to move him by arguments or threats, invokes the aid of a rogue lawyer to rid the parish of Fanny and get Joseph committed to gaol. But her schemes are interrupted by a visit from Squire Booby and his wife. This is an opportunity for bringing Pamela into the light of comedy. She feels that it would be a terrible come-down for her brother Joseph, the brother-in-law of Mr. Booby, to marry a girl of doubtful origin. Bat it is suddenly discovered that Fanny is the daughter of the Andrews and, therefore, Pamela is her sister and Joseph her brother. The disclosure gives scant joy to the impatient lovers. But a further disclosure sets everything right. Mr. Wilson reappears. Years ago, as he has already recounted, he had lost a son. That son is Joseph, who was stolen by gipsies and afterwards exchanged for Fanny, who was sold to Sir Thomas Booby. He is recognised by the famous strawberry mark on his left breast. He is as good a gentleman as Squire Booby himself. So both Pamela and Fanny have their wishes. Even that humblest of men, Parson Adams, comes in for a small fortune, being presented with a living of one hundred and thirty pounds a year.

Joseph Andrews has a thin but sufficient thread of plot on which are strung these consecutive scenes of jovial comedy. The major interest of the novel lies in the comic exposition of the follies and foibles of human nature or in the character of Parson Adams. The novel is in the picaresque tradition and Fielding himself described it as a comic epic in prose.

2. Jonathan Wild (1743)

The *History of the Life of the late Mr. Jonathan Wild the Great* is an ironical biography written in a tone of assumed admiration and applause. Jonathan Wild was a famous organiser of thieves. He was also an informer and had betrayed a number of accomplices to the authorities. He was hanged in 1725. His life offered interesting material to a number of writers including Defoe. Fielding used his fictitious biography only as a stalking-horse for satire on the human folly "that pays tribute to the kind of merit implied in the favourite saying, that 'nothing succeeds like success', and confounds together greatness and goodness." On the subject of greatness and goodness, Fielding says, "No two things can possibly be more distinct from each other, for greatness consists in bringing all manner of mischief on mankind, and goodness in removing it from them." But, as he ironically maintains, greatness is greatness wherever you find it; and in the career of a ruthless, unblushing, double-dyed scoundrel like Jonathan Wild you have the perfect example, with the perfect climax, the gallows.

Jonathan is the last member of a very ancient family of light-fingered gentry. He learns to thieve almost before he is out of the cradle and at school leads his friends on their marauding escapades. He is sent to the plantations as a convict. On his return from there, he manages to make himself the secret but despotic ruler of a gang of thieves who carry on their operations all over London. Wild himself never takes part in any robbery. He receives the booty, which he disposes of to the owners or other people, giving up only a small fraction of the amount realised to the actual thief. He shows his greatness by exercising a complete authority over his gang of thieves. If anyone of them shows signs of disobedience, he is immediately handed over to the authorities and hanged. Blueskin, for example, tries to keep a watch that he has stolen, instead of surrendering it to his chieftain, and puts himself at the head of a conspiracy of malcontents; whereupon Wild informs against him. Blueskin is committed to Newgate and Wild's control is reestablished.

Jonathan Wild also excels in emptying the pockets of his friends and cheating them at the gaming-table. He uses his talents even on the wily Count La Ruse, who cheats him at cards, but is himself robbed of his gains without being able to convict the friend (Wild) whom he knows to be the culprit. However, Wild is not so happy in his love affairs. He nurses a passion for Miss Laetitia Snap, daughter of the keeper of a gambling-house. On one occasion she rebuffs him with chaste indignation but as soon as Wild goes away lets another admirer out of the cupboard. He does marry this girl eventually.

An interesting episode in the novel is that of the Heartfrees. Heartfree is a London jeweller who has been a schoolfellow of Wild. Wild takes advantage of his complete honesty and his confidence in him to induce him to entrust a quantity of valuable jewellery to Count La Ruse, who runs away with it. Heartfree is even robbed of a large amount of money. Since more than half the jewellery is the property of other tradesmen, Heartfree is utterly ruined and is thrown into the Newgate prison. Wild has cast lascivious eyes on the poor man's wife, and now entraps her into fleeing with him to the Continent under the pretence of saving her husband from bankruptcy. He makes a forcible attempt to rape the lady but his purpose is frustrated through the intervention of the captain of the ship. They cast him adrift in a boat in order to punish him. Later he again tries to gain the confidence of his victim Heartfree, now languishing in jail. The jeweller, however, rejects his offer of aid; he is too good a man, and too timid also, to attempt an escape by murdering one or two of the keepers. Wild then determines to have Heartfree put out of the way and prepares a case against him on a false charge of fraudulent bankruptcy. Heartfree is found guilty and is on his way to the gallows when Mrs. Heartfree reappears. She has recovered most of the stolen property; and when Firebrand, a member of Wild's gang, turns against his chief and discloses the whole plot, the prisoner is released and the Heartfrees are restored to their former affluence.

At length, Wild is brought to book. He is tried, sentenced to be hanged, and being foiled in an attempt to cheat the gallows by taking poison, mounts the scaffold in the midst of an enthusiastic crowd, and with admirable firmness swings out of this world

Jonathan Wild is also written in the picaresque tradition. It is highly satirical, except that there is an element of the melodramatic in the episode dealing with the Heartfrees. According to E.A. Baker, "Grimmer satire than this cannot be found in English literature. The most corrosive pages in Swift's *Modest Proposal* or the last book of *Gulliver* are not more deadly." But it does not suggest Swift's cynicism. "It is the sardonic humour of a man," adds Baker, "who detests heartlessness and hypocrisy, but who never despairs of humanity even in a world that is black with turpitude."

3. Tom Jones (1749)

Brief outlines of the plot are given in the chapter *An Outline Summary of Tom Jones*'.

4. Amelia (1751)

Amelia is written in a tone slightly different from the one we find in *Tom Jones.* When Fielding started writing *Amelia,* he had behind him several years of experience as a magistrate in London. His spirit had received a shock, which did not embitter him but made him tenderer of heart, and less disposed to laugh at the frailties and disillusionments of mankind. In *Amelia,* there is less of irony; the prevailing attitude is one of discontent, impatience and indignation, tempered with pity for the victims of selfishness and folly. The ugly truth is denounced rather than held up to ridicule.

Booth is a military officer out of employment, who married Amelia for love. He failed as a farmer, and having shown a singular lack of prudence or of common ability to look after his wife and children, is now waiting for something to turn up. His appearance in the court of law, his conviction and consequent sojourn in gaol, are the first of a long series of misadventures, in which the truth and fidelity of the fond couple are tried. Booth in the end comes off successful with diverse adventures that do not quite finish him, and do not exhaust the patience of his wife. He is always loyal to his wife at heart, though sometimes out of weakness he gives way to temptation. His wife by her unexampled steadfastness foils all the conspiracies against her virtue and forgives his faults even when she has reason to believe him more to blame than he really is. But it is only through the intervention of their benefactor, Dr. Harrison and the sudden recovery of a fortune which Amelia did not know was hers, that they escape ruin.

This simple story is mixed up and made more absorbing with a number of episodes. First, Booth is entangled with Miss Matthews, an old love of his, whom he meets in jail. Thus thrown together, Booth and the corrupt lady yield to the temptation of the time and place, and when Booth is released, she refuses to give him up. The remorseful husband is henceforth in a continual state of fears lest his wife should hear of his faithlessness. His wretchedness is further increased when he learns that his friend and protector, Colonel James, is an unsuccessful rival for the love of Miss Matthews. With the Colonel only too sure to withdraw his support, and pretty certain to seek vengeance upon him, Booth sees ruin staring him in the face.

There are a number of other episodes introduced into the story to give it breadth and variety. Colonel James falls in love with Booth's charming wife, and now tries by fair means or foul to get her husband out of the way. Miss Matthews' affair has apparently blown over, Booth having promised to avoid the lady. Booth is the last person to suspect, even to imagine, that his most influential and trusted friend is the secret enemy of his domestic happiness. But there is another more dangerous plot also going on behind the scenes. A noble lord, with the help of the procures, Mrs. Wilison, in whose house the Booths are lodging, has designs upon Amelia. Amelia is put on her guard against his designs by a certain lady.

The couple are surrounded with a web of intrigue and Booth's rashness and Amelia's innocence are no safeguards against a host of snares. Besides this, the husband and the wife, unhappily, are not in each other's confidence. One thing or the other prevents their opening their minds to each other frankly. We catch them struggling in the dark. Amelia fears to let out all she knows lest her hot-headed husband should challenge the would-be seducer. When Booth's suspicions are at length aroused, first, as to the designs of the lecherous lord, and then to the treachery of his friend, the Colonel, he is stunned by the consciousness of his own fault, and by the repeated threats of the infuriated Miss Matthews to betray him to his wife, if he will not renew their contacts. The fear of insulting Amelia's perfect loyalty is enough to make him shrink from warning her against the designs of James and the lord who outwardly appears so blameless.

The climax is reached when the wicked Peer, finding all his plans and intrigues come to nothing, employs his regular pimp, Captain Trent, to entrap Booth. The unlucky youngman is induced to play at cards. The game ends with a debt of honour to the captain, and a few days later, as he is unable to pay the debt, he is clapped in a sponging-house, where his other creditors seize the opportunity to bring law suits against him. Amelia had stripped herself and the children of their ornaments and everything except what they had on their backs, and had managed to raise the fifty pounds owing to Trent. But out of his foolish optimism, Booth parts with the money to a certain great man who promises by his influence to secure him an appointment. The same day, Booth received an urgent letter from Miss Matthews threatening to tell his wife everything, if he does not call on her that evening. Poor Booth goes to her accordingly. The bailiffs arrest him at her door. And so Booth is back in jail, penitent and full of despair. That night, while Amelia is waiting for his return, she receives a note from Colonel James summoning him to a dual in the morning, for breaking his promise about Miss Matthews. It is followed by the news that her husband is arrested. She is really heartbroken.

Next day she receives a long letter from Booth explaining and confessing everything. She visits him in jail next morning, and he begs her forgiveness. She, of course, does forgive him. Miss Matthews carries out her threat to denounce Booth to his wife, but the violence of her resentment shows that she is the guilty party. Dr. Harrison soon arrives and bails out Booth. Then, with astonishing swiftness, justice is done all round. Amelia gets possession of her mother's property that was cunningly being appropriated to another. It was a lawyer Murphy who had played a prominent role in depriving Amelia of her due. Dr. Harrison promptly gets him arrested and the novel ends in happiness to the Booths.

3

The English Novel before Fielding

The rise of the novel in England, strictly speaking an eighteenth century phenomenon, was a result of the democratic movement. The phenomenal growth of commerce and industry under Robert Walpole's rule marked the decline of the feudal nobility and the rise of the middle classes. There was a tendency to dispense with the classical rigidity and restraint and an effort to search for a medium that allowed substantial freedom of expression to the emerging middle class writers. Poetry and drama, on account of the very nature of their structure, call for some discipline at least but the novel offered a fresh field in which the writers could enjoy unlimited freedom and they fell for it in quite a big way. The rise of the novel also coincided with the growth of a miscellaneous reading public with women forming one of its formidable and influential sections. Most of the historians of literature believe that novel as a popular genre began with Richardson's *Pamela* in 1740. However, a certain amount of prose fiction did exist in the sixteenth and seventeenth centuries also and it should not be out of place here to make a note of it.

Sixteenth Century: Sydney, Lodge, Lyly, Nashe

Most of the fiction in the sixteenth century was either romantic or didactic. Sir Philip Sydney wrote *Arcadia,* a romance of chivalric adventures in a pastoral setting. Thomas Lodge produced *Rosalynde* (1590) that formed one of the sources for Shakespeare's *As You Like It.* Robert Greene wrote *Pandosto* (1585) which Shakespeare used for *The Winter's Tale.* A didactic strain runs through the writings of Lyly, More and Bacon. Lyly, the most prominent among these wrote *Euphues* (1578) and *Euphues And His England* with very feeble plots but with brilliant discussion of manners. And his exposition of morals was so impressive that his work could serve even as a guide to civil behaviour. A realistic note was struck by Thomas Deloney. Thomas Dekker and Thomas Nashe. Deloney faithfully portrayed the life of the weavers in *Jack of Newbury* and that of the shoemakers in *The Gentle Craft.* Dekker also drew realistic sketches of the low life in London in some of his tracts. Thomas Nashe's adventure story *Jack Wilton* that had even some form in it came closest to the realistic novel.

Seventeenth Century: Aphra Behn, Bunyan

In the seventeenth century, the religious controversies, the social dissensions and the civil war consumed much energy of the writers. Still in the early decades of this century, there were written, under the French influence, quite a number of heroic romances, strange compounds of 'sham chivalry, sham pastoralism, pseudo-history and the extravagant gallantry of a sophisticated society'. These romances were entirely removed from ordinary life and though their appeal was primarily to the aristocracy, their immense popularity suggests that they were enjoyed by others also.

In the latter half of the seventeenth century, Mrs. Aphra Behn and several other women writers, in reaction against the absolute unreality of the earlier romances, cultivated a form of fiction that preserved the truth of life. Samuel Pepys and John Evelyn wrote diaries wherein they recorded the ordinary everyday details of their lives. What they wrote wasn't exactly novel, but it employed the type of material the novelists were bound to make use of.

The most important writer of the seventeenth century is John Bunyan. His earliest work *Grace Abounding* (1666) is a kind of spiritual autobiography. His other works are *The Pilgrim's Progress* in two parts (1678 and 1684), *The Life and Death of Mr. Baclman* (1680) and *Holy War* (1682). In *The Pilgrim's Progress,* Bunyan tried to project an allegorical vision of life, conceived as a journey. Bunyan had a penchant for a detailed description of scenery and lively, natural conversations. Hence his allegory is never dull, and his narrative, despite being loaded with spiritual meanings, moves on quite briskly. His style, with a marked Biblical tinge, has a charm of its own and is a great asset of Bunyan's art as a novelist.

Eighteenth Century: Defoe, Richardson

The most outstanding figure active in the field of novel writing in the early eighteenth century is that of Daniel Defoe. His important works include *Robinson Crusoe* (1719), *Captain Singleton* (1720), *Moll Flanders* (1722), *A Journal of the Plague Year* (1722) and *Roxana* (1724). *Robinson Crusoe* was inspired by the actual experience of Alexander Selkirk on an island. The novel reports Robinson Crusoe's adventure with admirable straightforwardness and ranks among Defoe's most popular works. *Captain Singleton* is a story of adventurous piracy. *Moll Flanders* depicts the amorous experiences of its picaresque, easily seduced, heroine. But Defoe's best work is perhaps *A Journal of the Plague Year* that gives a fictitious but exceptionally vivid account of the London plague of 1665.

Defoe rejected the fantastic conventions of the romance and adopted the manner and tone of actual biography. And yet his tales are so removed from actual life and character, and the element of adventure and crime is so prominent in them that they should, in all appropriateness, be classed as romances and not as novels. He wrote for the Puritan middle classes and there is a streak of didacticism in all his works, still his tolerance of the moral lapses of his protagonists is quite apparent. Defoe's audience enjoyed the adventurous stories of the criminals, pirates, and debauched prostitutes narrated in easy, plain and familiar language and felt quite satisfied with the didactic note, though at a very superficial level, with which these novels were concluded. His novels are marked by 'racy realism, sentimentalism and pious exhortation' and his habit of giving realistic details gives his works an air of verisimilitude but he lacks a sense of form and his plots are nowhere organically constructed.

This brings us to Richardson, who, quite accidentally, established the form of the novel as it is known today. He was asked by a publisher to prepare a series of model letters for general guidance and he wrote how to negotiate a proposal of marriage, how to apply for a situation, even how to ask forgiveness after having offended someone. Then it suddenly occurred to him that he could arrange these letters round a central theme and in 1740, he brought out his *Pamela or Virtue Rewarded.* This is the story of a virtuous maid-servant who resists the dishonourable advances of her master and is finally rewarded by a proposal of marriage from him. The whole action is unfolded through letters. The novel caught the fancy of the general reading public and he wrote *Clarissa* (1747) and *Sir Charles Grandison* (1753) in the same style. Richardson is not to be read for his stories, but his knowledge of the human mind, in particular that of the female mind, his delineation of the shades of sentiment as they shift and change and his exquisite skill in the creation of pathos have been rarely surpassed. He was also hailed as a great champion of virtue, but his utilitarian concept of morality—morality calculated to bring material advancement—though acceptable to the masses, aroused the indignation of Fielding, who parodied his *Pamela* in *Shamela* and partially carried the parody even in *Joseph Andrews.*

4

A General Introduction to *Tom Jones*

Tom Jones, Fielding's masterpiece and, in all probability, the greatest novel of the eighteenth century, was written between 1746 and 1749. S. Diana Neill describes it as 'a great novel in itself and a microcosm of the next hundred years in prose fiction'. Modern criticism, rational and liberated, acclaims its greatness in most unequivocal terms. But Fielding's contemporary society was sharply divided in their appreciation of its merits. While a number of readers admired it for the masculine vigour and the healthy morality of its author, most of them, devoted to Richardson's sensibility cult, could not rise above their own morbid sensibility and failed to appreciate it.

Outlines of the Plot

Tom Jones has such a complicated plot that it is just not easy to sum it up in a few lines. R.P.C. Mutter sums it up it thus: "The wealthy, benevolent Squire Allworthy, living in Somerset with his unmarried sister Bridget, returns one night from a three months' absence to find a baby lying in his bed. The child is adopted by Allworthy, given his own Christian name of Thomas, and the surname of the presumed mother, one Jenny Jones. Her former employer, the schoolmaster Partridge, denies the accusation of paternity, but his hysterically jealous wife gives evidence against him and he is dismissed from his post.

"Soon after the discovery of Tom, Bridget marries the unpleasant and grasping Captain Blifil; the captain dies two years later, leaving behind him a son, who is to become Tom's antagonist. Tom and Master Blifil grow up together under the tuition of the clergyman Thwackum and the philosopher Square. Nearby lives the fox-hunting Squire Western, his worldly and politic sister, and his beautiful daughter Sophia, with whom Tom falls in love. Western, however, is ambitious to secure the marriage of Sophia with Blifil, so that the estates can be joined. Tom's high-spirited escapades (which include an affair with Molly Seagrim, the far-from-innocent daughter of Black George the gamekeeper) are eventually used by Blifil to achieve the deception of Allworthy and Tom's expulsion from the household.

"At the same time, Sophia, to escape a forced marriage with a man she loathes, runs away; and the middle part of the novel is taken up with various adventures on the road—first as Sophia follows Tom's trail, and then, after the climactic events in the inn at Upton-on-Severn, as Tom pursues Sophia."

"Meanwhile Tom has, quite by chance, met Partridge, now set up as a barber-surgeon, and they go along together. He rescues a Mrs. Waters from attempted murder, and accompanies her to Upton, where he succumbs to her charms. It is only towards the end of the novel that Partridge identifies Mrs. Waters as Jenny Jones, and the horror of presumed incest is added to Tom's many other misfortunes."

"Finally all the main characters end up in London. Tom gets involved with the middle-aged nymphomaniac Lady Bellaston, whose crony Lord Fellamar attempts to gain Sophia by force. Fellamar also employs a press-gang to remove Tom, but their aid is made unnecessary by Tom's encounter with Fitzpatrick, a hot-headed Irishman, whom he had met at Upton and who now attacks him in mistaken jealousy. Tom wounds him—fatally, it is thought—and is arrested. With the press-gang prepared (at Blifil's instance) to give false witness against him, things look bleak for Tom; but at last the wheel of Fortune turns and brings him to the top."

Organisation

The novel is divided into three parts, each consisting of six books. The first six books lay the foundation of the story, and cover the time preceding Tom's birth to his unjust banishment by Squire Allworthy. The second part describes the several adventures of Tom and Sophia on their journey from Glastonbury to London. Here the novel takes a very rambling course, but it must be said to Fielding's credit that, except an incident or two, introduced to present a generalised contrast or a comment, all the episodes are well integrated with the development of the plot. The last six books take all the major characters to London. They cover little time but are replete with action. Fielding had many problems left in suspense for his denouement. He must punish Tom Jones for his breaches of good conduct, reveal the fundamental goodness of his character, lay bare the intrigues against him, and disclose the mystery of his birth. All this is done with great art, and the book ends happily with the marriage of Tom and Sophia.

In spite of F.R. Leavis's very scathing remarks (the conventional talk about the perfect construction of *Tom Jones* is absurd) it is generally granted that Fielding has managed his plot with consummate skill. It is a plot built on dramatic principles; it gains in momentum as Tom and Sophia follow each other on way to London; the climax is reached at the Upton Inn; then gradually the novel moves to its comic resolution. Coleridge was right when he said that *Tom Jones* had one of the three perfect plots ever planned, the other two being the plots of *Oedipus Tyrannus* and *The Alchemist.*

Epical Dimensions

Fielding himself described *Tom Jones* as a comic epic in prose. The novel, indeed, does possess epical dimensions. In the words of Aurelien Digeon, "the common characteristic of all the works which are usually called, and deserve to be called "epics' is that they express, at a given moment, the soul of a generation, in all its fullness and all its depth, perhaps in all the dimness of its hidden dream. ... A work is epic when it is the complete expression of a moment of collective life, a fragment of the legend of the centuries." Judged from this point of view, *Tom Jones* definitely gives the impression of an epic. "It is a picture of all England that we find there," says Digeon, "and a picture of England at a moment when, suspended between her great past and her prodigious future, she was most limpidly herself....... *Tom Jones* is the England of the time." Much of the Englisn society is portrayed in *Joseph, Andrews* as well as *Amelia.* But they do not give the impression of completeness. It is *Tom Jones* alone that gives the impression of fullness.

Moral Vision

Dr. Johnson said that he scarcely knew 'a more corrupt book than *Tom Jones*' and be rebuked Hannah More for quoting from 'so vicious a book'. According to him, no modest lady should have ever confessed that she had read *Tom Jones.* And yet the novel has a healthy moral vision to project. We have no reasons to doubt the intentions of Fielding when, in his dedication to George Lyttleton, he talks of 'the beauty of virtue' and says that 'to recommend goodness and innocence hath been my sincere endeavour' in the novel. But, without discounting the importance of chastity, he does not equate virtue with chastity. To him virtue is 'goodness of heart', and the greatest vice is hypocrisy. Hypocrisy is a mask and when the mask is ripped off, we get a very striking presentation of the contrast between the face presented to the world and the real features of a character. *Tom Jones* is full of hypocrites—the whole Blifil clan, Bridget Allworthy, Thwackum and Square, landlords and landladies, the servants of various ranks, the Seagrim family, Honour and Partridge, Mrs. Western and Mrs. Fitzpatrick, Lady Bellaston and Lord Fellamar, all are hypocrites. The two characters who distinguish themselves from this crowd by virtue of their honesty and integrity are Tom and Sophia. They wear no masks; their handsome faces are the index of their handsome souls. Tom does wear a mask at one or two unguarded moments—particularly when he rhapsodizes over Sophia's beauty and his own constancy but only a moment later retires into the thickest part of the grove with his old flame Molly Seagrim. But he has to pay for these lapses. It is precisely this incident that later leads to his dismissal from the Allworthy household. But while Fielding exhibits the loveliness of virtue and denounces vice (mostly in the form of hypocrisy) and emphasises the need of pursuing virtue and avoiding vice, he also dwells on the importance of prudence and circumspection in guarding virtue and it is this that constitutes his moral vision.

Humour

Tom Jones is a comic epic and the essence of comedy lies in humour. R.P.C. Mutter describes Fielding's humour as 'a broad, sane, extroverted humour, never malicious and never petty'. In *Tom Jones,* Fielding's humour takes many forms. There is the humour of action, a knock-about comedy of fights and horseplay, sometimes described in the mock-heroic vein, like the scuffle in which Molly gets involved, or the quarrel between Mrs. Partridge and her husband, or the fights at Upton Inn. Then there is the humour of character presented through characters like Squire Western and Partridge. Western is a complex figure of comic violence; Partridge is a mild version of Sancho Panza. Carefully manouvered entraces, exits and exposures also present a lot of humour. Square is discovered in Molly's room when she is vociferously articulating her love for Tom. Honour indulges in a bitter harangue against Lady Bellaston with the lady herself perched behind a curtain. Squire Western makes a dramatic appearance just when Lord Fellamar is about to rape Sophia. Tom, Sophia and Lady Bellaston run into one another at the residence of Lady Bellaston and pretend to be utter strangers. Sometimes a lot of fun results from two incompatible characters being brought together, say characters like Square and Thwackum. Occasionally, Fielding indulges in ironical humour also, humour at the cost of some characters. Bridget appears 'inconsolable' after the death of her husband with whom she has not shared even a single happy moment. Captain Blifil urges upon Squire Allworthy not to be soft towards a bastard child, himself carrying on an illicit affair with Bridget. But even while indulging in these ironical flings, Fielding is never cynical like Swift or Smollet. He seems to be like a man who understands the frailties of mankind and is willing to take a lenient view of them.

Realism

Fielding is described as a realist. But his is a selective realism. He does present us with a vivid picture of the eighteenth-century town and country life, but it is a selective picture. Fielding is not much interested in atmosphere or detail for its own sake. He gives us the bare necessities of external aspects. Allworthy's gothic house is lightly sketched in, and all that we know about Squire Western's estate is that it is adjoining. The life in London is described in great details, and yet Fielding is largely indifferent to the filth and squalor and stink of London. We visit Tom in the prison but the ugliness of the prison life is eschewed. The poverty of Mrs. Miller's cousin is described but we are hardly made to feel it. There are broad, generalised hints of the savagery, brutality and misery that seethed beneath the polite surface of the eighteenth century England but their horror is always kept under control by Fielding's comic and ironic vision.

Author's Comments

Tom Jones is full of the author's comments, but they are, fortunately, by and large, confined to the introductory chapters of various books. These chapters may be deviations from the story but they are so arranged that they may be read separately. And they are too good to miss. Fielding uses them to express his views on art and morality. He is conscious that he is giving a new genre of literature and he takes pains to describe its various aspects. He is also anxious to adjust the moral point of view of his readers to his own perspective of right and wrong. This is mostly achieved in the author's comments in the introductory chapters.

5

An Outline Summary of *Tom Jones*

Squire Allworthy, a childless widower, lives in retirement in Somersetshire along with his sister Miss Bridget Allworthy. One day on his return home after an absence of a full quarter of a year in London, he discovers an infant lying asleep in his bed. The discovery causes much flutter, but he decides to keep the child in his care. This foundling, named Tom Jones by the Squire, is the hero of the novel. Enquiries by Mrs. Deborah Wilkins, the Squire's housekeeper, reveal that one Jenny Jones who had lately nursed Miss Bridget in a violent fit of illness is the mother of the foundling. When questioned by the Squire, she freely confesses her sin but refuses to reveal the name of the father. Squire Allworthy gives her some wholesome admonition and makes her leave the neighbourhood. After Jenny's departure, the local schoolmaster Partridge whom Jenny had served for a while is suspected to be the father. Squire Allworthy summons him, reprimands him, and as a punishment deprives him of his annuity. Soon after, Partridge's wife dies and he also leaves the country. Miss Bridget marries Captain Blifil and eight months after the marriage, the couple is blessed with a fine boy, Master Blifil. It is decided that the new-born infant and Tom Jones, the foundling should be brought up together.

Squire Allworthy grows very fond of Tom Jones. Captain Blifil soon dies of apoplexy. The parson Thwackum and the philosopher Square who are incharge of the two youngsters, Tom and Blifil, lose no opportunity of maligning Tom in order to win the favour of Bridget. Blifil is a willing accomplice in these endeavours. However, sometimes it appears as if Bridget prefers the foundling even to her own son.

Tom, quite a mischievous lad, has Black George, the gamekeeper among his friends. The two are together involved in a poaching incident on a neighbouring estate belonging, to Squire Western, an ill-tempered boorish country squire. Tom, in order to save Black George takes the blame upon himself and helps his family in many other ways. These actions, though well-intentioned, are exploited by Blifil and the two tutors to tarnish his image in the eyes of Squire Allworthy.

Tom gets interested in two women, Black George's daughter Molly, an aggressive coquet and Squire Western's daughter Sophia, gentle, virtuous and generous. A series of incidents bring Tom and Sophia together and they fall in love with each other. But this puts Tom in a dilemma. Molly is found to be pregnant and Tom ascribes to himself the responsibility for her pregnancy.

Secondly, being a penniless bastard, he knows he cannot be acceptable to Squire Western who insists on a prudential marriage for his daughter.

A quick succession of events give a strange turn to Tom's life. A chance discovery of Square in Molly's bed-room absolves him from all moral responsibility towards her. But a few indiscretions committed by him give Blifil a chance to vilify his character and he is dismissed by Squire Allworthy. He takes the road to Bristol. A match is proposed between Blifil and Sophia and when Sophia is unduly forced to accept it, she decides to leave the protection of her father and go to London to one of her relations, Lady Bellaston.

Now Tom and Sophia are both on the road, separately of course. Tom desirous of joining the army, runs into a company of recruits and volunteers to join them, but offended by a bawdy jest by Ensign Northerton at the expense of Sophia, picks a quarrel with him and gets wounded. He meets Partridge, supposed to be his father, who denies that he fathered him but offers to accompany him on his wanderings. Tom rescues an old recluse, the Man of the Hill from being robbed by two ruffians and the very next morning he saves Mrs. Waters from being strangled by Ensign Northerton. He conducts Mrs. Waters to the Upton Inn.

The Upton Inn is the centre of some gripping drama. Tom Jones is seduced by Mrs. Waters. Sophia, accidentally reaching the same inn, quickly discovers Tom's involvement with Mrs. Waters and departs without meeting him. Squire Western, hot on her track, misses her by a few minutes and, lured by a fine hunting day, temporarily gives up the chase. Tom, remorseful for having missed Sophia through his own moral laxity, also leaves for London.

In London, Tom and Partridge take lodgings with Mrs. Miller. Her daughter Nancy, pregnant, is threatened with a rejection by her lover Nightingale. Tom prevails upon Nightingale to marry Nancy and saves Mrs. Miller's family from utter disaster.

Believing that it lies only in Lady Bellaston's powers to bring him in touch with Sophia, Tom allows himself to be seduced by the lady who is in reality a wealthy but corrupt society woman. But he soon gets fed up with this odious affair and on the advice of Nightingale, proposes marriage to lady Bellaston. The trick works, for the marriage nowhere being in the lady's mind, she breaks away and the affair comes to an abrupt termination.

In the last phase of the novel, Lady Bellaston plays a very crucial role. Sophia being the real object of Tom's attention, Lady Bellaston, with the purpose of getting her out of the way, persuades Lord Fellamar to rape her so that in her disgrace she might be forced to accept him as her husband. Sophia is fortunately rescued by the timely arrival of Squire Western who takes her in his own custody. Out of desperate malice, Lady Bellaston does two things. She uses Tom's letter of proposal to her to instigate Sophia against him. At the same times she plots Tom's abduction by a press gang.

A duel with Mr. Fitzpatrick lands Tom in the jail. His fortunes are now at the lowest ebb. Mr. Fitzpatrick's wounds being reported fatal, his very life is in danger. Mrs. Waters is found out to be Jenny Jones and Tom is given the appalling news of having committed incest. Lady Bellaston and Blifil, both acting independently, try to ensure that Tom is unable to secure his release from these circumstances. However, his friends, generously assisted by Lady Luck, are also at work. Mr. Fitzpatrick is declared out of danger and he confesses he was the first to provoke Tom. A death bed letter from a repentant Square and Mr. Miller's testimony to Tom's innate goodness reconcile him to Squire Allworthy. Blifil and Dowling are forced to confess their villainy. Jenny Jones gives out the secret of Tom's true parentage—he is the illegitimate son of Bridget from Summer, a former resident at Squire Allworthy's estate—and he is absolved from the sin of incest. Mrs. Miller, Squire Allworthy and Squire Western all intercede on his behalf and he is reconciled to Sophia as well.

6

Detailed Summary of *Tom Jones* with Critical Comments

BOOK I

Tom is discovered in Allworthy's bed; Jenny Jones confesses she is the foundling's mother; Bridget marries Captain Blifil.

Summary

In Somersetshire, in a commodious and venerable-looking house, there lived Squire Allworthy, who might well be called the favourite of both Nature and Fortune. 'From the former he derived an agreeable person, a sound constitution, a sane understanding, and a benevolent heart; by the latter, he was decreed to the inheritance of one of the largest estates in the country.'

Squire Allworthy was now an issueless widower, his wife having died five years before the beginning of the story and all of his three children having died in their infancy. He lived with his sister Miss Bridget Allworthy, a spinster past the age of thirty, 'whom you commend rather for good qualities than beauty'. She was a prude; she thought of personal charms in a woman as snares and was contemptuous of beauty.

One day, late in the evening, after an absence of nearly three months in London on some very particular business, Squire Allworthy came home. As he was preparing to step into bed, he beheld an infant, wrapt up in some coarse linen, lying between his sheets. Overcoming the initial surprise and moved by compassion, he summoned his 52 year old house-keeper, Mrs. Deborah Wilkins. Mrs. Wilkins was at first quite bewildered to see the infant. She, then, suggested that it should be put in a warm basket at the church warden's door, and they would have done their duty. But Squire Allworthy gave her positive orders to take the child to her own bed and bring it to him next morning.

Next morning, Squire Allworthy presented the infant to his sister Miss Bridget, who, contrary to all expectations of Mrs. Wilkins, commanded her brother's charity in what he had done, though she strongly condemned the poor, unknown mother of the foundling. She made so liberal arrangements for its care that she could not have exceeded them, had it been her own child. She said, since it was her brother's whim to adopt the little brat, she supposed it must be treated with great tenderness.

Mrs. Deborah Wilkins then went around to make enquiries about its mother. Her suspicion fell on Jenny Jones, not a very comely girl but endowed with good understanding improved by learning. She had lived with Partridge, a schoolmaster and was 'as good a scholar as most of the youngmen of the age'. Her superiority had provoked envy among her neighbours who thought her to be a dubious character. She had nursed Miss Bridget in a violent fit of illness and had been seen at Squire Allworthy's house just a day before his return from London. Jenny freely confessed to be the mother of the foundling.

When Jenny appeared before Squire Allworthy, he did not deal with her harshly. He exhorted her to lead a virtuous life saying that 'there is more pleasure, even in this world, in an innocent and virtuous life than in one debauched and vicious'. He assured her of making adequate provision for the child and asked her to reveal the name of his father so that he could be properly punished. Jenny, however, refused to divulge his name, saying that she was under religious vows and protestations to conceal it. Besides, the man was now out of his reach. Squire Allworthy was sorry but he did not insist. He dismissed her with the instructions that she was to be removed from the scene of her crime. Miss Bridget duly approved of this action. However, when the news of Allworthy's leniency reached the villagers, they sharply reacted against it. A whisper was soon abroad that Squire Allworthy was himself the father of the foundling child and even a legal enquiry was demanded. Allworthy remained oblivious of this invidious gossip.

Squire Allworthy was a very hospitable person. Particularly welcome at his house were men of merit. One among them was Dr. Blifil, whose one positive recommendation was a great appearance of religion. Miss Bridget was greatly attracted to him and the two would have married, but Dr. Blifil was already married, his wife was alive, and Squire Allworthy knew this.

Dr. Blifil, in these circumstances, thought of his brother Captain Blifil who had no such encumbrance. Captain Blifil was introduced into the Squire's family. He promptly caught his brother's hint, got enamoured of the Squire's house and gardens, his lands and tenements, and wooed Miss Bridget, who, after a token resistance, conceded to his suit and the match was made. Squire Allworthy, having full faith in his sister's discretion, made no objection. Rather, he appeared pleased with the match.

One of the Devil's maxims is, when once you are got up, to kick the stool from under you. Strictly in accordance with this maxim, no sooner was Captain Blifil possessed of Miss Bridget and reconciled to Allworthy than he began to treat his brother with increased coldness. This unaccountable ingratitude of the captain absolutely broke the poor doctor's heart. He went to London where he died soon after.

Commentary

Book I is introductory in nature. It introduces a few of the characters—Squire Allworthy, his sister Bridget, Mrs. Deborah Wilkins, Jenny Jones, Partridge, Dr. Blifil, Captain Blifil and the foundling Tom Jones.

Squire Allworthy is an instinctively good man. His benevolence is set off by the selfish Mrs. Deborah Wilkins and by the malicious and designing Blifil brothers. He is arraigned for his goodness and false motives are imputed to him, which is highly characteristic of this selfish, smug world and which suggests that the only sure reward of doing good is the consciousness of having done it. Dr. Blifil is a very minor character and appears to have been created only for the purpose of setting off Squire Allworthy's character. Tom Jones is just presented to us.

Bridget's extra-solicitousness of Tom is rather suggestive; so is Jenny's insistent refusal to reveal the name of the father of the foundling. We are supposed to accept the child as a bastard, though we are sure the mystery will be revealed in its good time. The unfolding of the action is highly dramatic. The discovery of the child, Allworthy's decision to adopt it, Bridget's acquiescence in the plan, Dr. Blifil's insinuation of Captain Blifil into the Allworthy family are all presented dramatically, Fielding's training as a dramatist serves him well. In fact, the entire structure of the novel is dramatic.

Captain Blifil's character foreshadows the ugly traits of character his son will exhibit in the novel.

BOOK II

Blifil is born; Partridge is accused of being Tom's father and dismissed; Captain Blifil dies.

Summary

Squire Allworthy grew quite fond of the foundling whom he had given his own name of Thomas. He seldom failed to visit him at least once a day.

Eight months after Bridget's marriage, she was blessed with a son, the delivery having prematurely taken place 'by reason of a fright'. Even the birth of this heir did not alienate the Squire's affections from Tom, and despite the Captain's opposition, it was decided to bring up the two children together. Meanwhile, Mrs. Deborah Wilkins continued her search for the father of the foundling.

It has already been noted that Jenny Jones had lived some years with a certain schoolmaster Partridge who had instructed her in Latin. He was a good-natured and pleasant fellow who made his living by working as a teacher, clerk and barber, this income being supplemented by an annuity of ten pounds from Squire Allworthy.

Mrs. Partridge was so jealous by nature that the least degree of civility towards any woman on her husband's part was sure to invite her wrath. Jenny had been working with the Partridges for about four years when one day at the dinner table, she happened to smile at the badness of a certain Latin phrase used by Partridge and having been caught in the act by her mistress, she blushed with the consciousness of having laughed at her master. Mrs. Partridge immediately fell into a fury and accused Jenny of whoring with her husband. A flabbergasted Partridge just sat staring and trembling in his chair. Jenny quietly packed off.

One day at an assembly of female gossip, Mrs. Partridge heard from someone that Jenny had been delivered of two bastards. Since Jenny had not been nine months gone away, she jumped to the conclusion that they must have been begotten at hers. She rushed home and flew at poor Mr. Partridge, her tongue, teeth and hands all in action. In pure defence, Partridge got hold of her arms to render them ineffective, at which she burst into tears and finally fell unconscious. When she regained consciousness, she complained of the manifold injuries she had received from her husband and drew the attention of the women to the blood on her face. Poor Partridge protested that this was blood from his face—in fact it was—to which the women said it was a pity 'it had not come from his heart instead of his face'. It was only after the company had left that Partridge came to learn why he had been thus battered.

Mrs. Wilkins, having got the scent of the above story, approached Captain Blifil, in whom she had perceived her next master, to inform him that she had at last discovered Tom's father. She also commented at her master's imprudence. The captain, pleased at heart, chid her for the liberty she had taken to revile thus her master.

Captain Blifil expected the story to reach Squire Allworthy, but Mrs. Wilkins, having been scared into silence by his earlier rebuke, made no mention of it. Finding the story in danger of perishing, the Captain decided to reveal it himself to the Squire.

Squire Allworthy was surprised at this news and Partridge was immediately summoned. The evidence of Mrs. Partridge, who was the chief witness and who was ready to take her bodily oath that she had seen them abed together proved decisive and Partridge's loud protests of innocence had no effect. He pleaded that at least Jenny's evidence be called for, but Jenny, having eloped with a recruiting officer a few days before, was to be found nowhere. Squire Allworthy dismissed as inconsequential the evidence that such a slut could have given and, convinced of Partridge's guilt, deprived him of his annuity and recommended to him repentance. Partridge and his wife fell upon evil days. Their condition would have been worse but for some charity from some good, unknown Christians, which it was felt actually came from Squire Allworthy. Partridge's misery was lessened only when his wife died of smallpox. He now left the parish. Meanwhile, Squire Allworthy's affection for Tom increased. It seemed as if he 'intended to counterbalance his severity to the father with extraordinary fondness and affection to the son'. This made Captain Blifil feel sore.

The marriage of Captain Blifil and Bridget was a marriage of convenience. Now with the passage of time, the bloom faded from their marriage. The Captain started treating his wife with haughtiness. She also started defying him in everything:

> If the one proposed any amusement, the other constantly objected to it; they never loved or bated, commanded or

> abused, the same person. And for this reason, as the Captain looked with an evil eye on the little foundling, his wife began now to caress it almost equally with her own child.

Thus there grew inveterate detestation in their minds. The Captain's sole delight was now to be lost into meditation upon the enjoyments that would accrue from Squire Allworthy's estate. But one day when he was lost in these contemplations, he had an attack of apoplexy and soon died. After his death, a splendid epitaph was' erected over his grave by his 'inconsolable' widow; this epitaph, among other things, eulogised him as 'a tender husband' and 'a devout Christian'; and this was a monument of 'his virtues and her affection'.

Commentary

This Book is described as 'containing scenes of matrimonial felicity in different degrees of life; and various other transactions during the first two years after the marriage between Captain Blifil and Miss Bridget Allworthy'. It deals with the married life of the Blifils on the one hand and that of the Partridges on the other. "Both the couples lead a wretched life. Only, the Partridges, being on the lower side of the society, do not wear the mask of gentility and culture. All their brawls take place in public reckoning, subjecting them to a scathing censure, whereas the Blifils manage to hoodwink their neighbourhood about the real condition of their married life and after the death of Captain Blifil, the widow is forced to appear 'inconsolable and to erect an epitaph in his memory'.

This Book also carries a discussion on charity between Allworthy and Captain Blifil. Allworthy, the acting Christian interprets charity as generosity and benevolent actions towards the poor and the wretched, but Captain Blifil, only a professing Christian argues that charity means the mere abstract holding of a high opinion of mankind. Captain Blifil is mean, malicious and hypocritical. By professing these abstract views he can pass for a true Christian at no personal cost. He goes by the letter of the law and ignores its spirit. He can quote and misquote scriptures wherever he likes.

BOOK III

> The contrast between Tom and Blifil; Tom lies to protect Black George; Thwackum and Square introduced; Black George dismissed

Summary

Tom Jones was now about fourteen. People around did not have any good opinion of him. In fact 'it was the universal opinion of all Mr. Allworthy's family that he was certainly born to be hanged'. From his earliest years he had shown a propensity towards vice and had already been convicted of three robberies.

When set against the virtues of Blifil, Tom's companion, his vices appeared in a more disadvantageous light. Blifil was 'a lad of remarkable disposition; sober, discreet and pious beyond his age'. While Tom Jones was universally disliked, the whole neighbourhood resounded with Blifil's praises.

About this time an incident happened that confirmed the opinion about Tom Jones. He went shooting with Squire Allworthy's gamekeeper Black George. The two spotted some partridges near the border of Allworthy's manor. But as they tried to shoot them, the birds flew over the boundary line. In defiance of the Squire's orders not to transgress any neighbouring estate, the two pursued the game and shot one of the birds. The owner of this estate, Squire Western, a hot-headed, extremely coarse individual, heard the shot and came flying towards it. Since Black George had conveniently hidden himself in a thicket, only Tom was apprehended and brought to Squire Allworthy. Despite Squire Western's persistent assertions that he had heard two shots, Tom denied there was anyone with him. Even a terrible beating from his tutor Thwackum did not make him confess the presence of anyone else. The thought that such a confession might lead to a loss of job for the gamekeeper made him resolve to be quiet. At last Allworthy was convinced of his innocence and in order to compensate the tortures he had suffered at the hands of his tutor, he presented him with a little horse as his reward.

Thwackum and Square were the two tutors entrusted with the education of the children. The two tutors were generally at logger-heads on all issues. But they had one similarity—they were both unredeemed hypocrites. In the composition of their several systems, Thwackum too much neglected virtue; and Square, religion. And both of them had utterly discarded all natural goodness of heart.

One day Master Blifil approached the two tutors with the complaint that Tom had given him a bloody nose. Tom defended himself by saying that Blifil had provoked him—he had called him a beggarly bastard. Blifil instantly denied the charge. How could he use such a naughty word, said he. He also slyly added he was not surprised at Tom's lying now since he was used to lying so often. Then he went on to relate the poaching incident and Black George's complicity in it—a fact that Tom had confided in him in good faith.

Both the tutors suggested that Tom should be given exemplary punishment. But Squire Allworthy could not be persuaded to punish him. Somehow, he appreciated Tom's fidelity. However, he resented the conduct of Black George, who had kept quiet and allowed Tom to be thrashed and dismissed him. Whosoever heard of the details of the incident considered Tom 'a brave lad' and condemned Blifil as 'a sneaking rascal'.

Square and Thwackum detested Tom for his being deficient in outward tokens of respect and for his lack of sobriety of manners and countenance. But there was still a stronger reason for their dislike of Tom. Little conscious of Bridget's preference for the foundling, they laboured wider the impression that their severity with Tom would win them favour with her. They interpreted her civility towards him as some scheme devised for his ruination. Mrs. Blifil, who had been disgusted with her first marriage, had no intention to remarry. She, however, liked to be flattered and hence kept the two hanging about her, showing such a preference for Square that malicious tongues soon started whispering.

With the passage of time, her preference for Tom became evident, and the more he rose in her favour, the more he lost favour with Squire Allworthy.

After Black George's dismissal, his family was almost on the verge of starvation. Tom sold two of his most valuable gifts given to him by Squire Allworthy—his pony and his Bible. A candid confession of this deeply moved Squire Allworthy, who exhorted Tom to approach him for such charities. Tom seized of this opportunity to press upon him the need of reinstating Black George, and Squire Allworthy would have relented if Blifil hadn't informed him of another poaching crime against Squire Western committed by Black George. Despairing of his honesty, Squire Allworthy abandoned him to his own resources. Tom decided to approach Squire Western, through his daughter, to appoint Black George as his gamekeeper.

Commentary

This Book covers about five years of Tom and Blifil's adolescence—fourteen to nineteen.

This Book clearly underlines Tom's goodness of heart and his unimpeachable sincerity in all his dealings and contrasts it with Blifil's treacherousness. At the superficial level, Tom is a born troublemaker whereas Blifil is 'sober, discreet and pious'. But below the surface, Tom is moved by very noble and generous impulses whereas Blifil is sneaking and hypocritical. His veneer of propriety and respectability hides a most villainously self-seeking heart.

This Book also introduces the two tutors, Thwackum the divine and Square the philosopher. Both of them are pompous fools; both of them are irredeemably hypocritical; and it is an ironical reflection on Squire Allworthy's moral blindness that the two are entrusted with the children's education when all they deserve is an immediate sack and kick. Thwackum is ever emphasising the divine power of grace but ever exposing his hypocrisy by his self-serving use of the Scripture. Square is indulging, *ad infinitum,* in his grand philosophical abstractions on the theme of virtue and his loud protestations of morality but miserably lacks an adequate perception of virtue and morality. Thwackum as well as Square is 'but an imperfect reflection in a distorted mirror of the true characters each of these classifications should represent'.

It would be misleading to think that Fielding justifies or exonerates Tom's imprudent involvement. He does not declare poaching a good activity. All that he wants us to understand is that it is a 'human' and 'natural' foible to indulge in such things, but Tom's goodness lies in the fact that once he is involved in them, he is perfectly sincere and he acquits himself creditably. His initial imprudence calls for censure; his later constancy should be extolled.

Similarly, Fielding does not discount the importance of philosophy and religion, nor does he reject them. But he does want to declare that good actions need good impulses and not just a knowledge of good principles. Mere familiarity with the letter of the text is highly inadequate; one must follow its spirit.

BOOK IV

Sophia introduced; The incident of the bird; Tom and Molly Seagrim; Molly's battle at church; Tom breaks his arm.

Summary

Sophia, Squire Western's eighteen year old, beautiful daughter was a middle-sized girl inclining to be tall. Her shape was not only exact but extremely delicate. Her mind was in every way equal to her person. She was sweet, innocent and even-tempered.

Tom Jones, when very young, had once presented Sophia with a little bird. Sophia, grown extremely fond of it, kept a small string about its leg and carried it wherever she went. One day, Blifil requested Sophia to trust it for a moment in his hands, and no sooner was he in possession of it than he freed it and tossed it into the air. Hearing Sophia scream, Tom ran to her help, and having been acquainted with what had happened, he immediately climbed up the tree on which it had perched. Unfortunately the branch snapped and he plumped over head and ears into a canal flowing below. The bird itself was caught by a hawk. Poor Sophia was naturally in tears.

On being questioned by Squire Allworthy, Blifil owned that he had released the bird 'for I always thought there was something very cruel in confining anything'. It was even unchristian, said he. Both Thwackum and Square praised Blifil's action as being in accordance with the highest sentiments of Christian charity, but Squire Western said Tom was as generous as Blifil was selfish and sneaking and 'if he was a son of his, his backside should be well flayed'.

Since this incident, Sophia's love for Tom had constantly increased. Since Tom had become a great favourite of Squire Western and hunted with him frequently, he met Sophia almost daily. Hence with her help, he got Black George appointed as Squire Western's gamekeeper. With the exception of Blifil, Square and Thwackum, everybody praised Tom's conduct.

Though Tom was not insensible of the charms of Sophia and her other qualifications, he felt himself bound to Molly Seagrim, Black George's daughter who was esteemed one of the handsomest girls in the whole country, and who had artfully seduced him with her coquetry but led him into the belief that *he* had seduced her.

Being moved by the misery of the family, Sophia had presented Molly with some of her discarded finery. One day Molly attended the church in a fine silken sack, which aroused the envy of her equals thereby making her the laughing stock of the whole congregation. After the service was over, she was physically attacked and there ensued a fight which Fielding had described in a fine mock-heroic style. Though Molly defended herself heroically, she would have been overpowered by her antagonists but for the timely appearance of Tom who rescued her from the vile attack, covered her with his own coat and safely conducted her home.

But the poor girl's cup of misery was not yet full. In this unfortunate broil, she had injured a travelling fiddler who, through Squire Allworthy, got issued a warrant against her. During her interrogation, her pregnancy was exposed, which made her liable to a far severer punishment. Tom was dining with the Westerns when he learnt from Parson Supple that on Molly's insistent refusal to reveal the name of her seducer, Squire Allworthy had decided to send her to the Correction House. He immediately rose from the table, begged to be excused and hastily left to see his godfather. This naturally led the Westerns to think that Tom was the father. Sophia was so shocked that she was suddenly taken ill and she could not see anyone else for the rest of the day.

Tom arrived just when Molly was being taken away. He immediately confessed that he was the father of Molly's child and pleaded to Squire Allworthy to inflict the punishment on him rather than on Molly. The Squire though grievously offended by his conduct was impressed by his candid confession. Molly was dismissed. Tom was given a serious discourse on the virtue of continence almost in the same vein in which Jenny Jones had been addressed twenty years before.

The episode evoked differed reactions. Thwackum gave a discourse on morality and unbended all his rancour against Tom. Square, a less violent but more artful person, insinuated that Tom 'supported the father in order to corrupt the daughter and preserved the family from starving to bring one of them to shame and ruin'. These considerations were 'too plausible to be absolutely and hastily rejected'. They certainly stamped in the mind of Allworthy the first bad impression concerning Jones.

Sophia who had been in love with Tom without knowing it herself now realised for the first time the depth of her emotion. But the affair with Molly pained her so much that she decided to avoid Tom. She started contemplating a visit to her aunt, but her father insisted that she accompany him to the 'hunt. It was on the hunt that once Sophia's horse bolted. Tom immediately sprang to her aid. She was saved unhurt but Tom's arm was broken. The arm was set and Tom was taken to Squire Western's home where he was put to bed. This naturally made a deep impression on Sophia's mind. Shortly afterwards, Sophia's maid, Mrs. Honour, caught Tom in the act of kissing Sophia's muff and reported the incident to Sophia: "He kissed it again and again and said it was the prettiest muff in the world." Sophia was now in love with Tom despite herself.

Commentary

Sophia is introduced in this Book. She is eighteen and already half in love with Tom Jones though quite unawares. She is modelled after Fielding's wife Charlotte Cradock and is portrayed in very soft colours.

In the incident of the bird, Fielding illustrates how the meanest of the motives can be made to look lofty when taken out of their context. Morality is not absolute. Evaluation of the moral content of human behaviour needs a careful consideration of the circumstances governing it as well as one's motives.

In the Tom-Molly affair, two points are worth noting. Tom is not the seducer, he is the seduced. In fact, when he discovers that he is developing a weakness for her, he resists visiting her for three months at least. But once he gets involved, he treats her with perfect honesty. He does not show even a moment's hesitation to go to his godfather and confess that he is the father of the child Molly is carrying.

The novel has a rich variety of characters. But the most memorable character is that of the fox-hunting Jacobite Squire Western. His speech and personal habits, his eccentricity and grossness have been drawn with utmost precision. The contradictions of his character are highly amusing; he loves his daughter but does not understand her; he thinks well of Squire Allworthy yet characterises him 'a queer B—ch'. He is a comic character and is slightly caricatured; still, by virtue of his sheer vitality, he dominates all the scenes in which he appears. In his presence, Squire Allworthy pales into insignificance.

BOOK V

Tom recuperates at Squire Western's; Square discovered in Molly's bed room; Allworthy supposedly near death; Bridget dies; Tom gets drunk to celebrate Allworthy's recovery.

Summary

During Tom's convalescence at Sophia's, she entertained him for hours together with the most delicious music at her harpsichord. It was now clear that both of them loved each other immensely. But this created a conflict in Tom's mind. He knew that in spite of Squire Western's love for him, he was a man of the world, so he would not approve of his addresses to his daughter. In fact, he had often said he wanted to see her 'married to one of the richest men in the country'. He also knew that Squire Allworthy would think it treacherous of him to propose marriage to Sophia. Finally, there was Molly, to whom he had sworn constancy. He spent many a restless hour, then finally he resolved to cling to Molly and think no more of Sophia.

But the resolution could not last long. Mrs. Honour told him how deeply Sophia now loved the muff that Tom had once kissed. She even retrieved this muff from flames when once, during a pique, Squire Western flung it into the fire. Tom now decided to meet Molly and offer her money and persuade her to forget him. He accordingly went to her house and tried to reason with her. Molly, in the beginning, was hysterical. She upbraided him for being insincere to her. But as she continued her harangue, there was discovered behind the arras philosopher Square, with Molly's nightcap on his head. Tom was at first bewildered to see him there; then he burst into loud laughter. He brought him out of his hiding place, promised that he would never expose him, and asked him to be good to Molly.

The infidelity of Molly would have led Tom to abandon her directly from his heart but the thought that he had himself originally corrupted her innocence made him very uneasy. But Betty, Molly's elder sister, told him that one Will Barnes had been the first seducer of Molly and the child that she was carrying was most probably Will Barnes'. The possession of this secret made Tom easy at heart and he now loved Sophia with unbounded passion. One day when Tom and Sophia accidentally met in the garden, they confessed their love for each other.

About this time Squire Allworthy fell ill and his physician declared him to be in danger of imminent death. The entire family was summoned round his bed and he made a discourse on how to meet Death. Then he made his will, leaving the most of his estate to his nephew Blifil, an allowance of £500 a year to Tom Jones and quite generous shares to others, though the others felt disgruntled at their shares. In the meanwhile there was announced an attorney from Salisbury with a special message. Blifil was sent to attend this attorney.

The attorney had brought the news of Bridget's death on her way home. Much against the doctor's wishes and much to Tom's chagrin, this news was immediately conveyed to Squire Allworthy. However, he had already turned the corner and was on his way to recovery. When Tom got this news, he was so happy that he got drunk and started singing. This led to a quarrel between Tom and Blifil.

After this unfortunate incident, Tom went to the fields to compose himself. It was a very pleasant evening and he was overcome by the thoughts of Sophia. His feeling that Sophia was beyond his reach filled his heart with despair. It was in these circumstances that there appeared on the scene Molly and after a brief parley with her, Tom retired with her into the bushes. Unfortunately, they were noticed by Blifil and Thwackum. Tom came out of the grove and confronted them while Molly stole out from the scene. Thwackum demanded that Tom should reveal the name of his companion. And when he refused, a stiff fight followed between Blifil and Thwackum on the one side and Tom on the other. It was Blifil who got the maximum thrashing.

In the meantime there appeared on the scene Squire Western, Sophia, her aunt and Parson Supple. Squire Western immediately came to Tom's assistance and the battle soon came to an end. Sophia fainted to see Tom bleeding and she was given all attention. The entire party except Blifil and Thwackum retired to Squire Western's home.

Commentary

Tom's dilemma in the beginning borders on the tragic. But it is resolved by Square's discovery in Molly's bedroom, an incident of a very comic nature. This pattern is often repeated in the novel. Whenever an episode threatens to be serious, Fielding gives it a delightful comic turn.

Dowling, the attorney who brings the news of Bridget's death seems to be an inconsequential character at this stage and his appearance (or non-appearance) almost goes unnoticed, but with his repeated appearance in the novel, he is going to assume greater importance and will play a key role in the final resolution at the end of the novel.

Tom's escapade with Molly has been treated satirically. Still Fielding does not forget to present some extenuating factors. Tom is drunk and Fielding remarks, "If there are any transgressions pardonable from drunkenness, they are certainly such as Mr. Jones was at present guilty of." Secondly, Tom has hardly any hopes of winning Sophia, so he naturally thinks 'one woman better than none'.

BOOK VI

Mrs. Western believes Sophia loves Blifil and the match is promoted; Sophia and Blifil; Tom is dismissed.

Summary

Mrs. Western was a perfect 'mistress of manners, customs, ceremonies and fashions'. She was excellently 'well skilled in the doctrine of Amour' but her masculine form was hardly suited to attract lovers. From Sophia's falling unconscious (described towards the end of Book V), she concluded that she was in love with Blifil and one day she decided to share her discovery with her brother. The news enraged Squire Western and he burst out, "How ! in love ! in love, without acquainting me ! I'll disinherit her; I'll turn her out of doors, stark naked, without a farthing." But when he learnt that she was in love with Blifil, he immediately cooled down. It was decided that he would himself propose the match to Squire Allworthy.

Squire Allworthy was due to dine with the Westerns. Sophia, apprehensive that Mrs. Western had suspected her passion for Jones, concealed her melancholy heart with the utmost sprightliness in her countenance and gaiety in her manner. She addressed herself to Blifil and took not the least notice of Tom. This thoroughly convinced Squire Western of her being in love with Blifil; he took Mr. Allworthy aside and very bluntly proposed the match. Mr. Allworthy, without any visible emotion, said that if the young people liked each other, he should be very desirous to complete the affair.

On his return home, Squire Allworthy communicated to Blifil the proposal made by Squire Western. He being utterly devoid of passion, Sophia's charms had not made the least impression on him, but he immediately thought of the gratification he would receive from the young lady's fortune and very cunningly answered that he was willing to submit to his fatherly care in all things. Squire Allworthy was not much pleased with this cold answer. However, he sent a confirmatory answer to Squire Western next morning.

Sophia was in her chamber reading when her aunt came in and broke to her the news of this confirmation. Under the impression that this had reference to Tom Jones, Sophia inadvertently let slip her love for Tom. Her aunt was stunned at the revelation and at the thought that Sophia was prepared to contaminate her family with an alliance with a bastard. However, she agreed to keep this love a secret on the condition that Sophia would entertain Blifil as a lover that afternoon.

That afternoon Sophia received Blifil as civilly as she could. The interview between him and Sophia lasted about fifteen minutes. Blifil expressed himself in a torrent of far-fetched and high-strained compliments which on her side were answered by downcast looks and civil monosyllables. Blifil took this behaviour as a modest assent to his courtship and appeared much pleased with this meeting. When he met Squire Western at the door, he looked elevated with success, which sent the old man into a frenzy of ecstatic joy. He was so affectionate with Sophia that she thought there could be no better moment to importune her father not to impose this relationship on her as she hated Blifil. He immediately got infuriated and threatened to disinherit her if she did not yield to his wishes. Then he left the room leaving Sophia prostrate on the ground, As he came into the hall, he came across Tom whom he immediately acquainted with the whole matter. He asked him to go to Sophia and do whatever he could. In a very touching scene, Tom requested Sophia not to marry Blifil. Sophia immediately said that she would never give him what was in her power to withhold from him. Mrs. Western told her brother in the meanwhile that it was actually Tom whom Sophia loved. Squire Western stormed back into Sophia's room and challenged Tom to a fight with him. Finding the Squire immune to all reasoning, Tom left his house for ever.

Next day Squire Allworthy was apprised of the true state of affairs. When Blifil learnt Sophia's preference for Tom, he got furious. He reported to Squire Allworthy Tom's conduct on the day when he was caught with Molly, maliciously distorting the entire sequence. His account was endorsed by Thwackum. Allworthy, accepting Blifil's story at its face value, regretfully dismissed Tom from his house.

After leaving the house, Tom gave way to utter grief and despair. Squire Allworthy had given him a note for £ 500 but Tom was hardly aware of it. In his despair he lost this note also. (Black George found this note and kept it for himself.) Before leaving the estate Tom sent a note to Sophia bidding her farewell and telling her to forget him. When Sophia received this note and the news of his dismissal from Mrs. Honour, she made available whatever ready money she had—sixteen guineas in all—and sent it to Tom.

Commentary

In this Book, the characters of Mrs. Western and Mrs. Honour, both of whom have already been introduced, are further developed. In a sense, both of them are comic characters.

Mrs. Western is devoted to her brother as well as to her niece. Her sense of propriety and norms of decency are strictly in conformity with the eighteenth century standards. Her constant dabbling with politics makes her a 'humours' character in the typical Jonsonian terms. She claims such a perceptive knowledge of 'the secret springs which move the great state wheels in all the political machines of Europe'. But she fails to fathom the 'rude, uninformed mind of a girl', Sophia, simply because Sophia is no typical eighteenth century heroine. In drawing Mrs. Western, Fielding had most probably in mind the two illustrious blue stockings of his times, Lady Mary Wortley Montagu and Mrs. Elizabeth Montagu.

Mrs. Honour adores her mistress but is equally awake to her own self-interest. In the middle Books, the Sophia-Honour relationship is going to assume a parallel importance to the Tom-Partridge relationship.

When Black George finds the five hundred-pound note of Tom, he keeps it to himself forgetting all the earlier generosity of Tom. This is treating his benefactor with deplorable insincerity and ingratitude, but it only retraces the pattern in which Captain Blifil had repaid his brother's kindness.

With Book VI, the first one-third of the novel is over. Life in Somersetshire has its limitations and in the interest of greater variety, Fielding must shift the scene of the story and take it to the highways leading to London and later to London itself.

BOOK VII

Tom sets out for Bristol; Squire Western and his sister press Sophia to marry Blifil; Sophia decides to flee; Tom joins a group of soldiers; Tom is hit in the head by a bottle.

Summary

The next morning Tom decided to go to the sea. He hired horses and set out for Bristol.

The same day Mrs. Western summoned Sophia into her apartment and began a long discourse on the subject of matrimony. She did not think of marriage as a romantic scheme of happiness arising from love; she considered it rather as "a fund in which prudent women deposit their fortunes to the best advantage, in order to receive a large interest for them than they could have elsewhere." Mrs. Western also referred to the honour of the great family to which she belonged, to which Sophia replied, "I shall never do anything to dishonour my family; but as for Mr. Blifil, whatever may be the consequences, I am resolved against him, and no force shall prevail in his favour." This was overheard by Squire Western who immediately flew into a passion and started reviling and berating Sophia. Mrs. Western objected to it on the grounds that this was a matter he had left totally to her negotiations. A quarrel ensued between the brother and sister and Mrs. Western threatened to leave the place.

Squire Western then turned to his daughter, spoke most violently against her, his sister and his late wife, and of the general ills he had received at their hands. Quite unwittingly, Sophia remarked that if her aunt had died the previous day, she was convinced she would have left him her whole fortune. This remark gave a sudden turn to Squire Western's thinking and he immediately rushed to beseech his sister not to go. Mrs. Western who really loved her brother needed no second persuasion to change her mind. Now both brother and sister jointly declared war against Sophia and proposed 'an immediate conclusion and execution of treaty with Squire Allworthy'.

Blifil was only too pleased at this. He was not devoid of lust. The agonies which affected the mind of Sophia augmented her beauty and the aversion to himself that Blifil had discovered in her added triumph to lust and served to heighten the pleasure he expected to derive from it. The idea of rivalling Tom Jones added another spur to his pursuit. The whole idea was so satisfying that he went the whole hog to realise it. He decided to deceive Sophia by pretending to love her and to deceive his uncle by pretending he was loved by her.

Mrs. Honour who had overheard the plans rushed to Sophia with the information. Sophia at first threatened suicide. Then she decided to run away. Mrs. Honour, in hope of future rewards decided to accompany her. She of course debated with herself whether it would be more profitable to betray Sophia to the Squire and gain an immediate reward or to accompany her mistress in the hope of a much larger reward later on. Finally she decided on a course of loyalty. She promised Sophia to meet her outside the house at midnight. Having planned this, Sophia pretended obedience to her father who, delighted with this, immediately gave her hundred pounds to buy some trinkets with.

Tom had hired a guide to conduct him to Bristol. Unluckily the guide was as unacquainted with the road as Tom himself and the two were hopelessly lost. They decided to stay at an inn for the night. A little later, a band of soldiers, on their way northwards to fight against the rebel supporters of the Stuart claim to the throne noisily entered the inn. They consumed large quantities of beer but no one seemed willing to settle the score. Tom, out of his patriotism and his sympathy with the established government agreed to pay the bill and also volunteered to join them.

Next evening he had dinner with some officers of the group. It was soon evident that his manners were much superior and he was not the matter out of which a common foot soldier is made. After dinner, the officers drank various toasts. Tom reluctantly proposed a toast to Sophia. Ensign Northerton, one of the officers present there, made a bawdy jest at Sophia's expense, which enraged Tom, and in the scuffle that followed, Northerton hurled a bottle of wine at him. Tom, bleeding from the head, fell on to the ground and lay there motionless. Ensign Northerton was taken into custody.

The surgeon who was summoned to dress Tom's wounds declared that Tom's life was in danger. In reality, however, Tom was in no grave danger. After a little rest, he felt strong enough to challenge Northerton to a duel in order to revenge his honour. Northerton had, however, made good his escape by bribing the landlady.

Commentary

Sophia has so far been a lovely but passive heroine and if she is to attract the same amount of attention as the hero Tom, she must shed off her protected position and come out as a fighter. By leaving her father's house, Sophia displays real courage. In Fielding's age, the dangers to be faced on the highways were really great and the thought of marriage with Blifil must be repulsive enough to drive her to take such a radical step. Besides, her age demanded from the children a degree of obedience inconceivable to us in the modern age. In addition, it must be remembered that in spite of being so crude and rough-hewn, Squire Western was a really loving and indulgent father, Sophia would be loath to offend him or to hurt him unless the provocation were a bit too strong.

In this book, Blifil's motive', in desiring to marry Sophia are also explained. He is moved by lust, greed and revenge. The prospect of marrying a girl who has been the beloved of Tom Jones as well as becoming the owner of the Western Estate is very alluring and in utter defiance of Sophia's feelings, he deludes Squire Allworthy into believing that Sophia loves him so much.

Squire Allworthy's blindness is just irritating. For a man of his position, his lack of perception and understanding is really deplorable. He appears to be but too willing not to be deceived. His absolutely uncritical trust in the hypocritical Blifil and his failure to recognise the real virtue in Tom ill becomes a man like Allworthy who also happens to be the magistrate in his estate.

Squire Western also deserves a little comment. That he loves his daughter is beyond any doubt. But he is a headstrong, despotic, domineering father who has never tasted marital felicity and who little realises what it is to marry without love. He has constantly Sophia's welfare in mind; he simply fails to comprehend wherein her welfare lies. For him affluence and social respectability are too important factors to be ignored in deference to any concession for sentiment.

BOOK VIII

The reappearance of Partridge and his decision to accompany Tom; They set out after the army; the story of the Man of the Hill.

Summary

When the landlady visited Tom, she rebuked him for having fallen out with those soldiers. Then she mentioned the name of Sophia. She said Sophia had often lain in the same bed in which Tom was now lying. In his rashness, Tom disclosed that he had been expelled by Squire Allworthy and was now penniless. At this, the landlady immediately made an excuse and flung herself out of the room.

When the physician arrived, the landlady told him to collect his fee immediately for Tom was penniless. In a violent dispute, Tom practically dismissed the doctor. The landlady, basically a good woman, agreed to give Tom his meals although the dinner had long been over. In the meanwhile Tom had a shave by the local barber.

The barber, called little Benjamin, was an odd fellow much given to jesting. In his talk he freely used scraps of Latin mostly incorrect. Tom in need of companionship was impressed by the candid talk of Benjamin and invited him to a drink. When Tom came to know that Benjamin had received a distorted version of his story from the landlady, he confided in him and told him the whole story barring only a circumstance or two.

Next morning, Tom realised that his wound needed further attention. He was told that the barber who had attended him the previous evening was also a good surgeon. Benjamin was summoned and he dressed his wound. Then he revealed his identity. He told Tom that he was Partridge 'who had the honour of being reputed your father, and the misfortune of being ruined by that honour.' Tom had always believed himself to be Partridge's son but Partridge said, "I hereby absolve you from all filial duty, for I do assure you, you are no son of mine." Partridge then said he had resolved to pursue him for he believed that Tom was born to make amends for all he had suffered on that account. Though Partridge offered this superstitious belief for his desire to accompany Tom Jones, he had indeed other motives too. He most firmly believed Tom to be Allworthy's son and he thought Tom had run away from his father. He thought that if he could prevail upon the youngman to return to his father, he would be rendering a service to Allworthy and might be reconciled him.

Partridge and Tom Jones came to Gloucester where they stayed at a famous inn, the Bell. Here Tom shared the table with two other guests, an attorney Mr. Dowling, who had brought the news of Mrs. Blifil's death to Squire Allworthy and another pettifogger who also claimed to be a lawyer. After Tom had left the room, this latter fellow gave the company such a highly sensational and, of course, untrue account of Tom's misadventure that when he came back, he found the landlady had turned hostile to him. Tom found the situation unbearable, and though it was about to get dark and Partridge was vehement in his protests, Tom decided to set out on his journey again.

The two companions came to the foot of a steep hill and Tom proposed to ascend it. Partridge was mortally afraid of meeting a ghost. Presently they spied a little glimmering light in a cottage and made for it. A hoglike woman who answered their knock told them that her master was not at home and was reluctant to admit them, for her master, the Man of the Hill, had given her very clear instructions not to admit anyone to the cottage. Just then, the sound of a scuffle was heard outside and snatching a broad sword hanging on the wall, Tom rushed out to save an old man from the clutches of two ruffians who were trying to rob him. This old man was the owner of the house. They came to the house together where the old man narrated a long story about his early life and his sojourn in the hills.

The Man of the Hill, when he was young, was sent to the university where he got addicted to gambling and drinking. From there he went to London where a notorious gambler Mr. Watson introduced him to the underworld. His father rescued him from this disgraceful life and took him back home where he spent the next four years in dedicated study.

After the death of his father, he happened to go to Bath where he again fell upon the notorious gambler now reduced to utter penury. He tried to rehabilitate him but his efforts were in vain.

In the meanwhile, the Duke of Manmouth rebelled against the king and the Man of the Hill, urged by his love for English Protestantism, along with Mr. Watson, the gambler, joined the Duke's forces. They took part in the battle of Sedgemore. Soon after, Watson betrayed him to the king's forces. He got a very severe shock. After travelling a good deal in Europe, he retired to this cottage in the hills and decided to lead a secluded life. He now dedicated himself to the study of religion.

Tom realised his feelings but tried to persuade him into the belief that the presence of one or two corrupt persons did not prove that the entire humanity was contaminated, and did not justify his generalised abhorrence of mankind. The old man, however, did not appear to be feeling convinced.

Commentary

At least a part of the mystery of Tom's parentage is solved in this Book with Partridge's disclosure that he is not Tom's father. For full revelation, we must wait till the last few pages of the novel.

Partridge, the little schoolmaster-barber-surgeon who, henceforth, will be a constant companion of Tom Jones has definitely been modelled after

Sancho Panza in Cervante's *Don Quixote* as was indeed Parson Adams in *Joseph Andrews.* There is a great affinity between the two: "Both are credulous and garrulous in the extreme, both follow their masters in hope of gain; both are home-spun; both frequently make penetrating comments on the behaviour both of their masters and society at large."

The long narrative of the Man of the Hill is usually dismissed as a pure digression—something that is irrelevant to the central movement of the novel. That it does not contribute to the development of the narrative cannot be denied. But a thematic contrast is definitely intended. The old man, having been wronged by humanity, weans himself from the active current of life and retires into a lonely abode among the hills. Tom has been wronged more grievously and has a greater cause for complaint. Still he keeps his faith in the goodness of man unimpaired. Withdrawal from society is a negative approach and is a sad comment on the potential dignity of man. Could the old man expect rescue at the hands of Tom if the latter too had followed the same approach ?

BOOK IX

Tom rescues Mrs. Waters from Northerton; Tom and Mrs. Waters at the Upton Inn; A fight in the mock-heroic style; Peace restored with the arrival of a carriage and four; Mrs. Waters seduces Tom

Summary

As the Man of the Hill finished his narrative, a lovely dawn was breaking and he invited Tom Jones to some fine natural spectacles of the countryside. They had just approached the fringes of the forest, when they heard, at a distance, the most violent screams of a woman. Without a word and despite the old man's attempts to check him, Tom ran down the hill and came upon a most shocking sight of a woman, stripped half-naked under the hands of a ruffian. He instantly fell upon the villain and sent him sprawling on the ground. The lady Tom rescued was a middle-aged one, with her face not very beautiful, but her well-formed and extremely white breasts that now lay exposed made up for her lack of beauty. Presently Tom noticed that the ruffian was no other than Ensign Northerton with whom he had earlier had a scuffle. He tied his hands on his back and returned to the Man of the Hill to seek his advice where he ought to go with the lady he had rescued. The old man advised him to go to Upton. Accordingly he took his leave of the old man and requested him to direct Partridge the same way.

When Tom Jones and his fair companion entered the Upton Inn, they were taken for some beggars and the landlady treated them with scant respect. Tom got enraged and a very comical fight ensued with Tom Jones and Partridge, who had also arrived, on the one side and the landlady, her husband and their amazonian maid Susan on the other. This fight was ended by the arrival of two decent-looking ladies who immediately went upstairs, and a company of soldiers. The sergeant immediately recognised Tom's companion as the lady of Captain Waters. The landlady was now repentant and she offered her a gown till she could get her own clothes. Mrs. Waters, at first disdainful of the landlady's apologies, was finally persuaded by Tom Jones to accept the gown and the two went to the dinner table.

No sooner had they sat down together than Mrs. Waters began to play her amorous artillery upon Tom Jones, who, however, attended only to beef and ale. When his hunger had been satisfied, he began to see the designs of Mrs. Waters and without duly weighing his allegiance to the fair Sophia, he succumbed to Mrs. Waters's display of her charms and 'the fair conqueror enjoyed the usual fruits of her victory'.

It is true that Captain Waters and Mrs. Waters had been living together, but there was some doubt that they were, in fact, legally man and wife. The Captain commanded the same company to which Tom had volunteered. Mrs. Waters had been carrying on some affair with Ensign Northerton and she had promised to meet him at Worcester when his division reached there. Northerton, however, got involved in an unfortunate affair with Tom and his life was still in danger. Mrs. Waters agreed to flee with him from the country. But Northerton, in order to obtain all her valuables, intended to strangle her at the foot of the hill. It was from this attack that Tom had rescued her.

Commentary

Book IX begins the most comic action at the Upton Inn, Tom's rescue of Mrs. Waters is again a tribute to the positive goodness of Tom Jones and a sad comment on the withdrawal from the society of the Man of the Hill, who shows absolutely no concern at the wails raised by Mrs. Waters. He just forgets that only the previous evening he has been the recipient of Tom's goodness which should have taught him to do good to others.

Tom has his second affair here. While Fielding will presently make Tom repent his incontinence, he definitely provides him with some extenuating circumstances. Once again Tom is the seduced rather than the seducer, for, on the dining table, Mrs. Waters has eyes only for Tom while Tom has eyes only for the excellent beef and ale in front of him. Secondly Tom has now fewer hopes than ever that he can meet Sophia.

Tom's battle with the landlady and his seduction by Mrs. Waters are two of the finest examples of Fielding's mock-heroic style in the novel.

BOOK X

Mr. Fitzpatrick arrives at the Upton Inn in search of his wife; A comic battle in Mrs. Waters's room; Sophia and Honour arrive; Sophia discovers Tom's affair and departs; Squire Western arrives.

Summary

It was midnight and was very quiet at the inn. Only Susan the maid was awake. An impetuous looking gentleman approached her and in a very abrupt and confused manner told her that he had come in pursuit of his lost wife and enquired if there was a lady in the house. Susan thought that he referred to Mrs. Waters and directed him to her room. The door was locked from inside but he violently broke it open. Tom Jones who was in bed with Mrs. Waters immediately jumped out of bed and demanded of the intruder who he was. The gentleman thought he had committed a mistake and was going to apologise when he suddenly caught sight of a lady's garments lying scattered on the floor. The two grappled with each other while Mrs. Waters cried 'Murder ! Robbery ! Rape !' An Irish gentleman staying in the adjacent room rushed in. He recognised Mr. Fitzpatrick and told him that the lady in the bed was not Mrs. Fitzpatrick.

The uproar had aroused the entire inn. The landlady too appeared at the scene. Mr. Fitzpatrick confessed his mistake. Mrs. Waters very shrewdly pretended that she was being attacked by Mr. Fitzpatrick and Tom had just rushed in to protect her. Tom also caught the hint and kept up the pretence.

It was hardly quiet again when two more guests arrived—a beautiful, richly dressed young lady and her maid. The two ladies were Sophia and Mrs. Honour. The former immediately retired to her room. The latter, in a very overbearing manner ordered dinner and then ridiculed everything, the inn, the landlady, the food served. This forced the landlady to defend the place. She said that this was no commonplace an inn. It was frequented by men of rank and fashion. Even then several important guests including the young Squire Allworthy were staying there. Since Allworthy was known to have no issue, Partridge explained to her that this was a reference to Allworthy's illegitimate son Tom Jones. At the mention of Tom Jones, Honour immediately rushed upstairs to inform Sophia.

After a hurried talk with Sophia, Honour returned to Partridge to tell him that her mistress wanted to talk to Tom Jones immediately. Partridge, irritated at Honour's earlier offensive behaviour and quite drunk at the moment remarked that 'one woman is enough at once for a reasonable man'. This was communicated to Sophia and duly verified by Susan. Sophia, grieved to learn all this, felt so exasperated that she decided to leave the inn immediately. Before she left, however, she bribed the maid to have her muff placed in Tom's bed.

Tom discovered the muff in his bed in the morning, having discovered how he had missed Sophia, he fell into cursing himself, Mrs. Waters and Partridge. Then he ordered horses.

Mr. Fitzpatrick and his Irish friend decided to hire the coach and four which had arrived the previous day. It suddenly occurred to the Irish gentleman that the lady who had come by this coach was none other than Mrs. Fitzpatrick. A hectic but vain search was again made for her. In fact, he had been a trifle too late in conducting the search. For Mrs. Fitzpatrick, alarmed by her husband's presence at the inn, had left almost at the same time as Sophia.

As Mr. Fitzpatrick returned to the kitchen, Squire Western, in pursuit of his daughter Sophia, burst into the room. Precisely at this very moment Tom Jones, with Sophia's muff in his hand, appeared on the scene. Squire Western immediately remarked, "We have got the dog fox. I warrant the bitch is not far off." Tom, who denied all knowledge of Sophia, was accused of stealing her muff and a legal machinery was improvised to try him for theft. Mr. Fitzpatrick, having discovered that Squire Western was his wife's uncle, in order to find favour with him, said that Tom had spent the night with her. Once again Mrs. Waters's room was knocked at, and though the misunderstanding was soon cleared, she decided to leave the inn, since she did not hope for any rest here. On Susan's testimony that Sophia herself had directed her to place the muff in Tom's bed, Tom was acquitted of the charge of theft. Squire Western, cursing everybody and taking the least notice of his nephew Mr. Fitzpatrick, immediately departed in pursuit of his daughter. In the violence of his hurry, and of his passion, he luckily forgot to demand the muff from Tom.

The conclusion of Book X is recapitulatory in nature. It gives an account of the events leading to Sophia's arrival at Upton. After leaving her father's house at night, Sophia had taken the road to London. But in order to avert being caught by her father she had taken a devious route in the direction of Bristol and unknowingly had fallen into the same path as her lover. This is how she had reached Upton when Tom was already there.

Commentary

Structurally, the episodes at the Upton Inn described in Books IX and X occur exactly at the centre of the novel.

All the important characters with the exception of Squire Allworthy and Blifil are brought together to produce high comedy. Mrs. Waters, an old familiar figure whose true identity is withheld for the time being is reintroduced into the action. Mr. Fitzpatrick, who is to play a key role in the final action, is also introduced into the action.

The roles being played by Tom and Sophia are now reversed. Hitherto Sophia has been following Tom. Henceforward, it is Tom who follows Sophia to London.

These Books, provide the much needed comic relief after the hazards of the road in Books VII and VIII and before Tom and Sophia once again plunge into the breath-taking action in the following Books.

Sophia's muff again appears in this Book and plays a very significant role:

(*i*) When Tom discovers it in his bed, he learns two things: Sophia has been seeking him; and Sophia has come to know of his infidelity.

(*ii*) Tom's appearance in the kitchen with Sophia's muff makes Squire Western believe that Sophia has already yielded to Tom. His belief is confirmed by Mr. Fitzpatrick.

(*iii*) Tom is accused of stealing Sophia's muff and a fine parody of law procedures in a court of justice is produced.

BOOK XI

Sophia meets her cousin Mrs. Fitzpatrick on the road; Sophia loses her hundred-pound note; Mrs. Fitzpatrick tells her story; The Irish nobleman appears; They all proceed to London.

Summary

Sophia and Honour, along with their guide left the inn at Upton and nervously rode towards London. They were soon overtaken by another party of three. Sophia, apprehensive of being caught by her father was terrified. To her relief, however, she discovered that the second party also consisted of two women and a guide.

The six riders rode on together for some time. The lady of the second party was experiencing some difficulty with her bonnet being blown by the wind. Sophia offered to tie the bonnet more securely with her handkerchief. The horse stumbled and Sophia was overthrown. Fortunately she escaped unhurt and the journey continued. As the day dawned, Sophia recognised that the other lady was Harriet Fitzpatrick, her cousin and Fitzpatrick's fleeing wife. The discovery brought much pleasure to both of them.

The two ladies reached a nearby inn and being exhausted decided to rest there. Here Harriet acquainted Sophia with her past life. Five years ago, Harriet and Mrs. Western were enjoying a holiday at Bath. Here she met an Irish gentleman Mr. Fitzpatrick and soon fell in love with him. Mr. Fitzpatrick pretended that he was courting Mrs. Western also in order to have an easy access to Harriet, a story that she easily believed, and married him. It was much later that she discovered that Mr. Fitzpatrick was in fact courting both the ladies and was trying to decide which marriage would prove a better financial catch. After her marriage, she was promptly disowned by Mrs. Western. Harriet was taken to Ireland where she soon found out that her husband was a dull, extravagant, faithless boor. Life in Ireland became intolerable. Mr. Fitzpatrick ill-treated her. Often he left her for months together. She lost her infant. She found out that her husband kept a mistress. When he decided to grab even the last relics of her fortune, she refused to surrender. At this he locked her in her room, swearing that she would either acquiesce or expire. However, she managed to bribe someone and make her escape. She was now flying to London.

Sophia also had to explain her presence on the road. She told Harriet why she had decided to quit her father's protection but made no mention of Tom Jones.

At this stage, an Irish nobleman came to speak to them. Harriet told Sophia that he was a 'friend' of hers and indeed was the same person who had helped her to escape from captivity. He offered them transportation to

London in his coach, and the offer was accepted. Although Harriet had greatly praised his absolute fidelity to his wife, Sophia observed during the journey that Harriet and her 'friend' were having an affair. She admonished Harriet for this affair and exhorted her to mend her behaviour. Harriet, however, treated this advice contemptuously. Sophia naturally decided to have nothing more to do with Harriet.

Sophia discovered that she had lost the bank note presented to her by her father. She had lost it, most probably, when she had fallen from the horse. Since nothing could be done about this also, she decided to go to Lady Bellaston. She was accorded a very cordial welcome there.

Commentary

Structurally this Book parallels Book VIII that preceded the peripety at the Upton Inn. That Book contained a slight digression in the narrative of the Man of the Hill. This Book too contains a digression in Mrs. Fitzpatrick's account. But as Book VII, by contrasting Tom Jones with the old recluse, underlines Tom's courage and nobility, the dubious account of her cousin brings out the virginal purity and nobility of Sophia.

Mrs. Fitzpatrick's account also provides a comment on Mrs. Western's character. She has been so critical of Sophia's love for Tom Jones but she forgets that she has herself been a victim to the worst kind of a debauched adventurer like Mr. Fitzpatrick. Only Harriet's presence at Bath had saved her from a very disastrous match.

BOOK XII

Squire Western gives up the pursuit of Sophia and joins a fox-hunt; Tom and Partridge move on to London; Tom meets Dowling, a band of gypsies and a highwayman along the way.

Summary

Squire Western had left the inn in pursuit of Sophia. But he soon ran into a hunting party and was tempted to join them. His prowess and skill at hunting were recognised by all and he was invited' to join them at dinner and drink. Next day, he was persuaded to go home.

Tom, highly disconcerted at missing Sophia had also left the inn a few minutes after the departure of Squire Western. He now intended joining army. But the cowardly Partridge gave a number of arguments to dissuade him. He even adduced scriptures. But Tom was adamant. They were interrupted by a wretched beggar. Tom gave him a shilling. Encouraged, he showed Tom a little gilt pocket book, the book that Sophia had lost and that contained within it the hundred pound bill also. Tom was overjoyed to find the bill. The beggar demanded half the amount of the bill, but Tom told him that since the bill belonged to someone else, he would have to wait for his reward.

As they neared a town, they heard the beating of a drum and although Tom tried to assure Partridge that the discovery of the pocket book had driven all thoughts of joining the army from his mind. Partridge felt frightened, for he thought that they had accidentally come across the rebel army and he was sure that Tom would enlist himself. However, it turned out to be a drum beating for a puppet show. So they decided to have their food and visit the show.

Tom went to bed with two of his companions, Sophia's muff and her pocket-book. He was soon awakened by a scuffle between the puppet show owner and his Merry Andrew. Rushing to the spot, Tom came to learn that, the very previous day Merry Andrew had saved a beautiful young lady from being robbed and raped by his master. Tom was sure that this young lady was none other than Sophia and the Merry Andrew conducted him to the exact spot of the incident. From there Tom and Partridge continued alone till rain forced them to take shelter at an inn. Here Tom met the postboy who had acted as guide to Sophia. He agreed to conduct them to the inn where he had left Sophia. Partridge was happy that Tom was on Sophia's trail rather than in search of an army.

At the inn, Tom was disappointed to learn that no horses were immediately available. However, he had a chance meeting with the attorney Bowling. The two had a friendly conversation over drinks. Bowling, unknowingly, referred to Squire Allworthy as Tom's uncle but Tom immediately corrected him.

When the horses got ready and they resumed the journey, they came upon a band of gypsies and were invited to attend a gypsy wedding. Partridge got drunk and was caught in a compromising position with one of the gypsy women. Partridge was allowed to escape unpunished but the gypsy woman was taken to task for having come so far and her husband for having connived at it. Both Tom and Partridge were surprised at this mode of gypsy justice.

Tom and Partridge proceeded to St. Alban's, only to find that Sophia had left the place two hours earlier. They now decided to move towards London. On the way, a highwayman, having come to know from Partridge that Tom carried a hundred-pound bill threatened him, at the point of pistol, to surrender the money. Tom was not prepared to surrender anything belonging to Sophia. In the struggle that followed Tom overpowered the highwayman who soon confessed that his pistol was unloaded and that he was an honest fellow but had been driven to such undesirable means by the poverty of his wife and children. Tom gave him two guineas from his own scanty allowance and exhorted him to help his family through more honest means. Then they proceeded to London,

Commentary

Exactly like Blifil and Thwackum earlier, this time it is the comical Partridge who demonstrates how 'the best principles can provide a shield for selfish motives'. Partridge appeals to Christian charity to prevent Tom from joining the army but forgets all about it to give a severe rebuke to a lame beggar who asks for alms.

The puppetmaster also talks of morality in arts but first his clown Merry Andrew is caught in a compromising position with the alehouse maid and later it is pointed out that the puppetmaster himself had attempted to rob and rape a very pretty lady.

Tom has another meeting with Dowling and the latter, inadvertently, does refer to Squire Allworthy as 'your uncle' but Tom, unsuspectingly, just corrects him and the revelation of the mystery of Tom's parentage is put off.

Partridge invites another comment towards the end of this Book. He has been persuading Tom to get Sophia's bill encashed without ever realising that would be 'legalised theft', but when the highwayman makes an attempt to rob Tom of this bill and Tom overpowers him, Partridge urges upon Tom to kill the highwayman.

BOOK XIII

Tom searches for Sophia in London; Tom seduced by Lady Bellaston: Mrs. Miller, Nancy and Mr. Nightingale; Tom meets Sophia at Lady Bellaston's.

Summary

At London, Tom, first of all, went to the Irish peer's house. From there a footman conducted him to Mrs. Fitzpatrick's house where Sophia had been staying temporarily. Unfortunately, he missed Sophia just by ten minutes. Mrs. Fitzpatrick, suspecting that he was perhaps Blifil or someone else sent by Squire Western refused to tell him the whereabouts of Sophia.

Her maid, however, told her that it must be Mr. Jones. Harriet immediately thought that if she could save Sophia from this imprudent marriage, she could get herself reconciled to her uncle whose favour she had lost by her marriage to Mr. Fitzpatrick. She accordingly went to Lady Bellaston with whom Sophia was staying. Lady Bellaston agreed that Sophia must be saved from Tom but said, that she could not do this until she had personally seen Tom. She had heard very high praise of Tom's handsomeness and also expected him to be thoroughly experienced in sexual manners. She decided to call on Mrs. Fitzpatrick that very afternoon when Tom Jones was expected there.

That evening Tom came to meet Harriet and told her that he wanted to see Sophia only to return the hundred-pound bill. Their talk was interrupted by the arrival of Lady Bellaston and the Irish peer. The Irish peer, feeling jealous of Tom's handsomeness rudely dismissed Tom and forbade Harriet to meet him again.

Tom and Partridge had taken lodgings with one Mrs. Miller, with whom Squire Allworthy used to stay during his visit to London. Tom had almost just retired to his room when he heard a noise downstairs and rushed down in time to save the tenant at first floor, Mr. Nightingale from being strangled by his servant—the two had quarrelled over the servant's rude behaviour to his master and his misuse of the apartment. Mr. Nightingale, who was having an affair with Mrs. Miller's elder daughter Nancy, and Tom Jones soon became close friends.

Next morning while Tom was at breakfast with Mrs. Miller, her two daughters and Nightingale, a maid-servant brought in a surprise package for Tom. The package contained a domino, a mask and a masquerade ticket; and it was supposed to have been sent to Mr. Jones from 'the queen of the fairies'. Tom was quite certain that it had been sent by Mrs. Fitzpatrick and it gave him hope that he would be able to see Sophia also at the ball.

At the masquerade, Tom approached every masked woman in hope of getting a glimpse of Sophia. Finally one of the masked ladies slapped him on the shoulder and whispered, "If you talk any longer with that trollop, I will acquaint Miss Western." The mention of Sophia's name made Tom follow the lady and he repeatedly requested her to tell him where he could find Sophia. The lady took him aside and began to flirt with him so openly that he was forced to pretend interest in her. Tom had also to follow her to her place where he discovered that it was Lady Bellaston and not Mrs. Fitzpatrick. Tom was seduced by Lady Bellaston that very night.

Lady Bellaston gave Tom fifty pounds, apparently to help him but actually as compensation for the sexual gratification she had received from him. In the evening Mrs. Miller told Tom the distressing tale of the family of one of her relatives. And Tom was so moved that he offered Mrs. Miller the fifty pounds he had received from Lady Bellaston. Mrs. Miller accepted ten guineas. Later, when this distressed relative of Mrs. Miller came to thank him personally, it was revealed that he was the same highwayman who had earlier accosted him. Tom was grieved to know how poverty could drive such an honest man to such undesirable means.

Meanwhile the affair with Lady Bellaston continued. Since the two were meeting at some place other than the Lady's house, although Sophia was staying with her, Tom and Sophia could never meet. But the owner of the house having turned Methodist, this house was closed to them and since Lady Bellaston had fallen for Tom a bit too passionately, she decided to invite him to her own house.

On the day of the assignation, Lady Bellaston sent Sophia away to the theatre. But the plan misfired. She herself got detained in another part of the town and Sophia, on account of a riot at the theatre came home early. Therefore, quite unexpectedly, Tom and Sophia came across each other at Lady Bellaston's. Sophia was so surprised that she was about to faint. So Tom had to support her in his arms.

A touching scene was enacted by Tom and Sophia. Tom apologised to her for his escapade with Mrs. Waters at the Upton Inn. Sophia did not mind this as much as the bandying of her name at so many inns on their way to London. Tom was able to convince her that the responsibility for this lay more with Partridge than with himself. Sophia was convinced and a very touching and tender love scene had just begun between the two when they were interrupted by the entrance of Lady Bellaston.

On this occasion, all the three acted very cleverly. Lady Bellaston pretended she had never seen Tom before. Tom caught the hint and acted as if he had seen both Sophia and Lady Bellaston for the first time. He pretended that he had come only to return Sophia's pocket book containing the hundred-pound bill. Sophia also pretended she had never seen Tom before. Before Tom left the place, he sought Lady Bellaston's permission to visit the place again. Lady Bellaston assured him that her doors were never shut to people of quality. After Tom's departure, Lady Bellaston pestered Sophia with a volley of questions about Tom but Sophia insisted that she did not know him.

Commentary

Book XII takes Tom agonisingly close to Sophia in London to begin the last act of the drama. Presently Squire Allworthy, Squire Western, Blifil and Jenny Jones will all be transported to London to bring about the final resolution. After the leisurely movement of the middle section of the novel, there is a definite feeling of crowdedness of events in the last six Books and this feeling begins with Book XIII itself.

This Book introduces Lady Bellaston, a middle-aged lady, affluent enough to keep a series of youngmen for her sexual gratification. She is cursed with foul breath and is frantically trying to prolong the pleasures of her fast withering youth. She is devoid of any moral scruples and one wonders if Fielding wants his readers to accept her as a representative of the eighteenth century aristocracy.

Book XIII presents Tom's third sexual involvement in the novel—it is also the most disgusting. Tom accepts £ 50 from Lady Bellaston and the reader is shocked at the degradation suffered by him. He is almost reduced to the level of the kept man. Isn't it ironical that when he apologises to Sophia for his affair with Mrs. Waters, the poor girl does not know that he is guilty of a worse kind of indiscretion with Lady Bellaston ?

However, Fielding immediately deflates this shock:

> Jones had never less inclination to an amour than at present; but gallantry to the ladies was among his principles of honour, and he held it as much incumbent on him to accept a challenge to love as if it had been a challenge to fight.

Secondly he succumbs to Lady Bellaston because he feels that it lies within her power only to bring him in touch with Sophia. Finally, Tom offers the whole of the money he gets from Lady Bellaston to Mrs. Miller so that the distressed family of the Andersons may be relieved.

BOOR XIV

Lady Bellaston develops an increasing passion for Tom; The history of Mrs. Miller; Nightingale leaves Nancy; Tom persuades Nightingale to return; Tom visits Nightingale's father.

Summary

Tom had just been home when he received two notes from Lady Bellaston, one gentle, the other furious, but both passionate. She had instructed Tom to come to her at once and as Tom was preparing to do so, the Lady herself appeared. She was afraid that Tom had betrayed her to Sophia. As Tom was trying to allay her fears, Partridge came with the news that Mrs. Honour was coming with a message from Sophia. Lady Bellaston hid herself hurriedly behind Tom's bed.

No sooner did Mrs. Honour appear than she started attacking Lady Bellaston's scandalous morals. She of course delivered to him Sophia's letter. Tom could quieten her only after he had given her a large tip.

When Lady Bellaston came out of her hiding place, she was furious and she blamed Tom for having spoiled her reputation. She also demanded Sophia's letter. Tom somehow tried to pacify her and kept back Sophia's letter from her saying that a lady's secret should be safe with a gentleman. Lady Bellaston remained with Tom till two in the morning and while leaving Tom, she took from him a promise that in future he would visit her under the pretence of paying a visit to Sophia.

Sophia's letter, however, put him in a dilemma. Sophia had requested him not to visit her lest he should arouse suspicions. Tom was really at a loss what to do. So he wrote a letter to Lady Bellaston feigning illness.

Next morning Tom found himself in difficulty with Mrs. Miller. The prolonged visit of Lady Bellaston had offended her. She was afraid that this would bring notoriety to her house and her daughters. She also disclosed that she knew of Tom's relationship with Squire Allworthy. Tom said that he would change his lodgings.

Nightingale also wanted to change his lodgings. His father was coming to London to arrange his marriage with a wealthy girl, so he wanted to break with Nancy. Nightingale and Tom decided to shift to the same lodgings.

At tea both Mrs. Miller and Tom Jones related to each other their history. Mrs. Miller had been a widow saved by Squire Allworthy's generosity. He had settled on her an annuity of fifty pounds a year; and also given to her this house to make additional money by renting it out to lodgers. Tom gave her his whole history, of course, without any reference to Sophia.

The next morning, Tom was awakened by an uproar downstairs. Partridge brought to him the news that Mrs. Miller was frantic, for Nancy had been found pregnant while Nightingale had left bidding her farewell. Tom went downstairs and tried to console Mrs. Miller. He assured Mrs. Miller that he would do his best to bring back Nightingale.

Tom found out Nightingale and had a long talk with him. Nightingale confessed that he had seduced Nancy by promising her marriage. He wished he could honour his promise but he was afraid of his father, who, he was sure, would not approve of his match with a penniless girl. Tom said that he would go and meet his father and try to convince him.

Tom quickly found out the elder Nightingale also. He found him a thoroughly materialistic man. Very cleverly Tom told him that Nightingale and Nancy had already been married. The elder Nightingale was almost struck dumb.

At this point, Nightingale's uncle also arrived. He knew that the girl chosen by his brother was extremely unpleasant. So he tried to inject some good sense into his mind. But this irritated the old man all the more. At this, the brother said that he at least would try to do for his nephew whatever he could. With these words, he left for Mrs. Miller's house with Tom.

When they arrived at Mrs. Miller's, the scene there had changed. Nightingale had returned and they were about to celebrate a wedding feast. Mrs. Miller was feeling grateful to Tom for having saved her family. But when Nightingale's uncle came to know that the marriage had not actually taken place, he immediately changed. He took away Nightingale to his own lodgings. Mrs. Miller and Tom were naturally uneasy over Nightingale's departure like this. Their tension was increased by the arrival of Mrs. Honour who had brought some 'dreadful news' about Sophia.

Commentary

The early part of Book XIV recalls a scene already witnessed in Molly's bed-room (Book V, chapter 5) when Square, the philosopher was discovered behind the curtain by Tom. This draws upon a conventional theatrical device to produce some boisterous fun and will shortly be repeated with a slight variation in Book XV, chapter 7 when both Mrs. Honour and Lady Bellaston seek the same hiding place in Tom's room.

Much of this Book deals with Mrs. Miller's domestic drama. Nightingale-Nancy affair is a clever variation of the Tom-Sophia affair. Nightingale takes pride in his ability to deceive women where as Tom always allows himself to be easily seduced on account of his weakness for sex. Tom is unacceptable to Squire Western because of his poverty. On the other hand, though Nightingale would like to marry the penniless Nancy for love, he is afraid of his father who would not approve of a marriage from which no material advantage can accrue to him. The Nightingale-Nancy affair on the one hand sets off the nobility of Tom, and on the other, it emphasises the prudential values of the age.

BOOK XV

Lord Fellamar and Lady Bellaston plan Sophia's rape; Sophia's timely rescue by Squire Western; Nightingale and Nancy marry; Tom proposes marriage to Lady Bellaston; Arabella Hunt proposes marriage to Tom.

Summary

Mrs. Honour had brought to Tom Jones a really dreadful news about Sophia.

On the day there was a riot at the theatre, Sophia was escorted home by a certain nobleman Lord Fellamar. This lord had passionately fallen in love with Sophia. Lady Bellaston, on account of her growing jealousy of Tom's affection for Sophia decided to make use of Lord Fellamar to make Tom her own. Lord Fellamar, having come to know that Sophia's father was a rich Squire, was already feeling enthusiastic about the affair. In order to whet his passion, Lady Bellaston told him a distorted version of Sophia's love for Tom. "He is a beggar, a bastard, a foundling, a fellow in meaner circumstances than one of your Lordship's footmen." On the same day, while playing whist, a concocted story about a man named Jones who had been killed in a duel was related to Sophia who immediately collapsed in her chair. This proved beyond any doubt Sophia's love for Tom and Lord Fellamar thought Sophia must be saved from that beggarly bastard.

Lady Bellaston's plan was an ingenious one. Lord Fellamar should rape Sophia, then to save her reputation should offer to marry her. Sophia will naturally be obliged to accept this proposal. Lord Fellamar was reluctant to follow this proposal but Lady Bellaston over-rode all his objections and at seven o'clock in the evening when Lady Bellaston had contrived to send away every servant from the house, Lord Fellamar was introduced into Sophia's room.

Sophia was reading in her room when Lord Fellamar entered and requested Sophia to grant his suit. When Sophia resisted his advances, Lord Fellamar used force. Sophia was about to be raped when Squire Western, followed by Parson Supple and others burst into the room with a loud noise. (He had learnt of Sophia's whereabouts from Mrs. Fitzpatrick's letter.)

The Squire who was quite drunk was about to attack Sophia and forcibly carry her to his lodgings when Lady Bellaston entered. She quickly discovered that Sophia's marriage with Blifil could equally serve her purpose, so she did not object. Lord Fellamar did try to intervene and press his own suit, but was rudely insulted. When Mrs. Honour offered to accompany Sophia, she was dismissed on the spot. Now Sophia's marriage with Blifil appeared certain. This was the dreadful news Mrs. Honour had brought.

While Tom was feeling grateful to God that Sophia was still alive and Mrs. Honour was feeling disgruntled that Tom had shown no sympathy for her over the loss of position, Partridge announced Lady Bellaston. Mrs. Honour had naturally to hide herself behind the bed.

A minute later, Lady Bellaston entered the room and immediately grew amorous. Tom, on account of Mrs. Honour's presence in the room, had to pretend ignorance of the hints in Lady Bellaston's voice. Just then, Nightingale, almost dead drunk, tried to enter the room. Perhaps he took this to be his own room. Terrified, Lady Bellaston also tried to go behind the bed but found the place already occupied by Mrs. Honour. Lady Bellaston was the one more afraid, for she thought she would lose her reputation. So she asked Honour to come to her the next day, and perhaps she would be able give her a position. Then the two ladies went away separately.

The next morning, Nightingale and Nancy were married. When Tom returned from the wedding he found three letters from Lady Bellaston. He told Nightingale that he wanted to end his affair honourably. At this, Nightingale, who had been in London much longer than Tom, told him that he need not suffer from any scruples on account of Lady Bellaston's honour, for she was notorious for keeping men and had no honour. Still, Tom said, Lady Bellaston had saved him from starvation and he was so obliged to her that he could not betray her. Nightingale then suggested that he should propose marriage to Lady Bellaston, and he was sure she would herself cry off in a moment. Nightingale himself dictated the letter and almost immediately it was answered back. Lady Bellaston had written, "I see you are a villain. And I despise you from my soul. If you come here, I shall not be at home." This brought the affair to an end.

Mrs. Nightingale received a letter from Squire Allworthy that he was on his way to London with his nephew Blifil and would like to occupy his usual room. Tom agreed to vacate the room and stay with Nightingale and Nancy for the time being.

Tom received two more letters; one from Honour in which she had announced having taken a position with Lady Bellaston, the second from a rich and beautiful widow Arabella Hunt proposing marriage to Tom. Tom politely declined the proposal.

Next, Partridge came into the room with the news that he had met Black George with Squire Western, and being one of the Squire's favourite servants he would be able to convey Tom's message to Sophia.

Commentary

This Book starts thrashing out the whole affair. The Nightingale-Nancy affair is concluded to the satisfaction of all. Even Tom-Lady Bellaston affair appears to be over. Squire Western and Black George are already in town. Squire Allworthy and Blifil have been announced. Mrs. Waters and Mr. Fitzpatrick are about to reach London. Events are happening breath-takingly fast and the final resolution looks quite imminent.

The threatened rape of Sophia should not have alarmed the reader. Lord Fellamar's sensibility is not sufficiently crude to pose any real threat and it should be obvious that it could at the worst be a verbal rape only. Sophia's sentimentalism over the distressed heroine of the novel she is reading supposed to set the mood of the scene, is also described in a comic style. Squire Western's fortuitous arrival to rescue his daughter makes it amply clear that Fielding had no intentions whatsoever of introducing tragedy.

This book throws light on one of the uglier sides of the eighteenth century. In the eighteenth century, an honourable man considered it disgraceful to marry a girl who had lost her chastity even if he were himself responsible for this tragedy of hers. That is why Lord Fellamar thinks that Sophia would feel grateful to him if he offered to marry her even after he had raped her. And that is why Nightingale is reluctant to marry Nancy even though she is carrying his own child. This aspect of the situation is presented in Richardson's *Clarissa* also.

BOOKS XVI

Sophia in the hands of Squire Western and his sister; Squire Allworthy and Blifil in London; Lady Bellaston plots Tom's ruin; Tom wounds Mr. Fitzpatrick in a duel and is arrested.

Summary

Sophia was taken to Squire Western's lodgings at the Piccadilly and kept there almost like a captive.

The next morning while the Squire was sitting at breakfast, a messenger from Lord Fellamar came to meet him. In a very comical scene, the messenger said that Squire Western should either render an apology for his rude behaviour the previous evening or agree for a duel. The Squire said that he would never permit Sophia to marry a lord and he had no time for duelling. He also dubbed his visitor as a liar. The messenger struck him repeatedly on the head, said that the Squire was utterly beneath his contempt and left.

Hearing an uproar Sophia had screamed, and the Squire rushed to her room. He pressed her to accept Blifil for her husband and put an end to all his troubles. He turned a deaf ear to Sophia's pleadings and arguments. Sophia, however, clearly said that she would never accept as odious a man as Blifil,

At dinner time, through the agency of Black George, a letter from Tom was conveyed to Sophia in the body of a pullet. In this letter, Tom had expressed his undying love for Sophia and wished her happiness in life with or without him. The letter consoled Sophia a good deal.

Mrs. Western arrived there, condemned her brother for making a captive of Sophia and removed her to her own lodgings to be kept under her direct supervision. From here Sophia wrote to Tom Jones telling him that she would never marry anyone else. Tom felt happy and relieved to receive this letter and that evening he went to see *Hamlet* with David Garrick in the title role. The evening became memorable on account of the highly ingenuous comments made by Partridge, who could not even distinguish illusion from reality.

Squire Allworthy and Blifil had reached London by this time. Squire Allworthy had learnt a little of Sophia's aversion for Blifil and was reluctant to pursue the case. Blifil, however, eager to consummate the match, immediately went to Squire Western, who took him to his sister. But no sooner was Sophia brought into his presence than she turned pale and speechless. At this Mrs. Western took them to task for having intruded upon their privacy and asked them to come again 'at a proper time'.

In the meanwhile, Lord Fellamar who had felt highly enamoured of Sophia approached Lady Bellaston again. The Lady said that if this proposal was to prosper, it was imperative to take care of Tom. At this Lord Fellamar agreed to contrive a plan so that Tom could be pressed and sent to the sea. At the same time Lady Bellaston called on Mrs. Western and pressed Lord Fellamar's suit. The very idea of having Sophia married into nobility appeared irresistibly charming to Mrs. Western. Lady Bellaston also gave Mrs. Western Tom's letter of proposal telling her to use it as she deemed fit.

Tom went to see Mrs. Fitzpatrick, whom he had met at the theatre the previous evening. Since she had no success with either Squire Western or his sister, she wanted to take revenge from them. So she suggested to Tom to pay respects to Mrs. Western and under this cover to try to see Sophia. Tom refused to pursue this dishonest course. Mrs. Fitzpatrick was so struck with this nobility of Tom that she got infatuated with him and threw him broad hints of this passion. Tom returned from there resolved in his mind never to see Mrs. Fitzpatrick again.

As Tom left the place and came out, he ran into Mr. Fitzpatrick whom he immediately recognised as the person who had burst open Mrs. Waters's room at the Upton inn and greeted him in a friendly manner. But Mr. Fitzpatrick, suspicious of Tom's relations with his wife, struck him on the head and there followed a duel between the two. Mr. Fitzpatrick was seriously wounded. In the meantime the press gang put into service by Lord Fellamar arrived there. Tom was arrested and conveyed to a magistrate. When a surgeon declared that Mr. Fitzpatrick's wound was fatal, he was put into prison. Here he got that news that Mr. Fitzpatrick had died. The final blow was delivered by Partridge who had brought a letter from Sophia. She had written that she had read Tom's letter of proposal to Lady Bellaston and she never wanted to see him again or even hear his name.

Tom's fortunes were now at the lowest ebb.

Commentary

There is nothing much to comment upon in this book. In conspiring with Lord Fellamar to get rid of Tom, Lady Bellaston is motivated by two considerations. She has been stung at Tom's breaking away and the very thought of another woman enjoying his manhood is highly unpleasant to her. Secondly, she wants to get out of her way a man intimately acquainted with her morally depraved life.

It must be said in praise of Fielding that he never lets his action slacken and lose its grip. And his reversals are manipulated with great skill. Precisely at the moment when Tom is feeling elated by Sophia's affirmation of abiding fidelity and boldly resists Mrs. Fitzpatrick's amorous advances, which in quality are not very different from Mrs. Waters's or Lady Bellaston's, he is put into prison, with the additional torture of denouncement at Sophia's hands. There could not be a more dramatic reversal of fortunes.

Partridge's ingenuous and entertaining comments at Garrick's performance of *Hamlet* are a great tribute to the histrionic ability of the great eighteenth century artist. So perfect is his rendering of Hamlet's dilemma that illusion looks little short of reality.

Having turned down an attractive marriage proposal from Arabella Hunt and successfully resisted Mrs. Fitzpatrick's passionate hints, Tom appears to have gained that emotional stability, continence and maturity, for want of which he has been put to great humiliation and self-torture in the past. He now fully deserves to win Sophia's hand in marriage.

BOOK XVII

> Squire Allworthy and Blifil in London; Mrs. Miller defends Tom; Mrs. Waters visits Tom and tells him Mr. Fitzpatrick is out of danger.

Summary

Squire Allworthy and Mrs. Miller were at breakfast one morning when Blifil joined them and very complacently remarked that Tom was one of the greatest villains alive. Mrs. Miller took exception to this remark and Squire Allworthy had to intervene to restore peace. However, he told Mrs. Miller that he regarded Blifil as one of the sincerest friends to Tom Jones and he did not like Mrs. Miller's criticism of Blifil. Blifil then broke the news that Tom had killed someone in a duel. Mrs. Miller still defended Tom by saying Tom could not have done so without some very strong provocation.

Just then Squire Western entered in a very furious mood. He had just learnt of Lord Fellamar's suit to Sophia and his sister's inclination to promote it. However, he asserted he was dead against nobility and Sophia would either marry Blifil or he would put her on the barest sustenance.

For the first time, Squire Allworthy realised how deeply Sophia detested Blifil. He declared that he could not be a party to this match. He did not like to force children into distasteful marriages and contribute to their ruin. But all this was beyond Squire Western's comprehension and he still claimed absolute authority over his daughter. At this stage, Blifil intervened and said he would like to take one more chance of winning Sophia's love, for she would not be able to love Tom once she learnt he was a murderer. This news made Squire Western so happy that he went capering about the room. Before taking leave of Squire Allworthy, he invited him to dinner. After his departure, Squire Allworthy subjected Blifil to a long discourse and advised him to give up his pursuit of Sophia. "It is certainly a vulgar error," said he, "that aversion in a woman may be conquered by perseverance."

Mrs. Western kept pestering Sophia to accept Lord Fellamar's suit, for she believed it could open up numerous channels for the family's aggrandisement. Sophia said she disliked Lord Fellamar as much as Blifil and related to her aunt the accident of the intended rape. She also flattered Mrs. Western into good humour. Consequently, she did not leave Sophia alone with Lord Fellamar when the latter came into Sophia's room for an interview, with her, though the interview had been arranged by Mrs. Western herself. But Mrs. Western could not be kept long in this cheerful mood.

Mrs. Miller and Nightingale visited Tom in prison and tried to console him. Partridge brought the news that Mr. Fitzpatrick was still alive. Mrs. Miller also agreed to convey a letter from Tom to Sophia. But this letter having been written in remorse contained only a confession of his own unworthiness and did little good to Tom when Sophia was ultimately persuaded to read it.

That evening, Mrs. Miller again had a long conversation with Squire Allworthy. She acquainted him with Tom's loss of five hundred pounds, his generosity with the Andersons and the role he had played in saving her own family from utter disaster. She also said that she considered Tom a better man than Blifil. Allworthy, enraged at this, said he would not stand Blifil's name being slandered and even threatened to leave the place. However, he soon controlled his temper, felt he had softened down towards Tom and also agreed to approach, on Nightingale's behalf, the elder Nightingale whom he knew from some business dealings in the past. This conversation was interrupted by the appearance of Blifil and Dowling.

Sophia once again angered her aunt by her persistent refusal to marry Lord Fellamar. Her anger was increased by Tom's letter to Sophia that Mrs. Miller had earlier brought. She said that she was returning Sophia to her father's protection.

Tom was still having a gloomy time. Nightingale who had been investigating the duel brought no reassuring news. He said that the sailors who had been present at the scene swore that Tom had struck first and that also quite unprovoked. Another gentleman present there had requested them to be truthful since a man's life was at stake but they still stuck to this very testimony. Tom had to reconvince Nightingale of his innocence in this affair. Just then Mrs. Miller arrived. She first talked of Sophia's indifference to his letter and then said that Mrs. Western had broken off all chances of communication with Sophia. Tom felt very unhappy to learn all this.

The third visitor to Tom was Mrs. Waters. She had been living with Mr. Filzpatrick as his wife, but she felt Tom had still 'power' over her. She had brought the news that Mr. Fitzpatrick was quite out of danger and at least on this, score Tom was quite safe. Mrs. Waters had relieved him of one particular worry, but Sophia's persistent indifference was still keeping Tom very sad.

Commentary

Squire Allworthy's voluntary offer to approach the elder Nightingale on his son's behalf reveals his inherent goodness and establishes an affinity between the Squire and Tom who has already gone on the same errand. His credulity, his firmly-rooted faith in Blifil and his strong prejudice against Tom is irritating though it must be admitted that this weakness humanises his character and makes it more probable. His confession that he has felt a softening of heart towards Tom is promising.

The arrival of Blifil and Dowling together suggests that the latter, in some way, has become an accomplice in the former's contrivances to ruin Tom. Presently, we shall learn that the 'other gentleman' who had prevailed upon the seamen to be 'truthful' was none else but Dowling who had actually been sent there by Blifil in order to pervert the evidence against Tom.

BOOK XVIII

> Partridge believes Tom has committed incest with Mrs. Waters since she is actually Jenny Jones; Mrs. Waters reveals to Allworthy 'the truth of Tom's parentage; Blifil is exposed by Dowling; Tom and Sophia marry.

Summary

While Tom was sitting in the prison in a dejected mood on account of sophia's indifference, Partridge burst into the room with a horrifying news that the lady with whom Tom had gone to bed at Upton Inn was in reality Jenny Jones, supposed to be Tom's mother and Tom had been guilty of the grave sin of incest. Mrs. Waters could not be traced out personally but Tom received from her a note which almost corroborated Partridge's news.

Just then Black George brought the news that Sophia had been conveyed back to the custody of her father who had been in rapture on two accounts—Sophia had refused to marry Lord Fellamar and Tom was going to be hanged.

The next morning Squire Allworthy went to meet the elder Nightingale and made him agree to pay a visit to his son. During the conversation it was also revealed that Black George had approached him with bills worth five hundred pounds. Squire Allworthy immediately realised that it was Tom's money and asked him to keep this a secret till he received further notice from the Squire himself.

Allworthy came home and told Mrs. Miller of what had transpired at the Nightingale's. Meanwhile the news was brought that Mr. Fitzpatrick was completely out of danger and his confession that he had challenged Tom to a duel had absolved Tom from all responsibility. Both Nightingale and Mrs. Miller sang praises of Tom; Squire Allworthy too appeared to have undergone a change of heart and he narrated to them some incidents from Tom's childhood.

A letter from Square also contributed to the Squire's change of heart. Square had written from the deathbed. He had testified Tom's generosity of heart, his capacity for friendship and his integrity. He had also written that great injustice had been done to him on account of 'the baseness of another person'

Now further details came into light. Nightingale had discovered Lord Fellamar's plot to have Tom pressed onto a ship. Mrs. Miller announced that Squire Allworthy's attorney Dowling had been in touch with the sailors whc had given evidence against Tom Jones. Squire Allworthy was thunder-struck at this. He sent for Blifil and Dowling to come to the root of the matter. Blifil was available and he admitted that he had sent Dowling but said that he wanted to soften the evidence against Tom. The gullible Allworthy was convinced and no harm was done to Blifil. He proposed a visit to Tom in the prison, but the arrival of Partridge prevented this visit.

In a private interview with Squire Allworthy, Partridge told him that he was not Tom's father. He also gave him an account of his wanderings with Tom and finally let out the secret of Tom's incest. The Squire was horrified.

At this very moment, Mrs. Waters entered the room. She was in fact Jenny Jones. In another private interview with the Squire, she told him that she was not Tom's mother, hence no incest had been committed. Then she disclosed the secret of Tom's parentage. Tom, like Blifil, was the son of Bridget. Tom's father was a handsome youngman Summer, who had lived at the Allworthy estate for about a year. The child was placed in Squire Allworthy's bed on the night of his return from London and she was bribed to own the guilt. She also told Squire Allworthy that Dowling had approached her and offered her money to prosecute Tom for the murder of Mr. Fitzpatrick. Squire Allworthy was appalled at the villainy of Dowling but he soon realised that he could have done this only at the instance of Blifil.

Now Blifil was completely exposed with the help of Dowling. Dowling had brought the secret of Tom's parentage to Squire Allworthy but he being on death-bed the letter was given to Blifil. Blifil had later told Dowling that Squire Allworthy wanted to conceal this secret from the world.

Tom was released from the prison and had a touching conciliation with Squire Allworthy. He pleaded with the Squire on two scores. He requested him to be lenient with Blifil and Black George.

Though Sophia was indifferent in the beginning, the pleadings of Mrs. Miller, Squire Allworthy and Squire Western who had turned a staunch supporter of Tom, softened her a little. The wedding was soon celebrated and Tom and Sophia lived happily everafter.

Commentary

So the play is over and the curtain has been dropped. Tom is at last blessed with some abiding peace and happiness. But he fully deserves it. He was always virtuous but lacked discretion to guard his virtue. Now that he has cultivated discretion and developed resistance to the stress of his carnal desires, he can confidently pledge steadfastness to Sophia and, in turn, be assured of love and loyalty leading to marital bliss. This is the moral point of view so convincingly upheld by Fielding. Tom begins as a bastard and though in deference to the eighteenth century notions of respectability, Fielding gives him a noble birth (Do Bridget and Summer deserve to be called noble ?), it would have made little difference to his modern readers even if he were left a bastard. He is a gentleman not by birth but by deeds and it is deeds that count.

In the prefatory chapter to Book XVII, Fielding promises that whatever be the fate of his hero, he would not violate the rules of probability or possibility. And true to his promise, although he seeks generous assistance of good luck, and invoking the authority of a comic-writer, he makes free use of coincidence, he does not overstrain one's credulity.

It should not be out of place to pause a little and look back to realise with what consummate skill Fielding has handled the intricate web of incidents. Details that looked trivial, incidents that looked digressive and characters that looked irrelevant have all their significance in the overall design of the novel. In the prefatory chapter to Book X, Fielding has already given us a warning that it would be pompous and absurd to presume to find fault with the parts before the design of the whole is known.

7

List of Important Characters in *Tom Jones*

Tom Tones

The hero of the novel; supposed to be a foundling but ultimately discovered to be the son of Bridget and a gentleman by the name of Summer; he grows up into an extremely handsome, well-formed, powerful young man; he is also generous, brave, courageous and kind; the goodness of heart is his main quality; he is guilty of indiscretions in the beginning but gradually learns to control his exuberant animal passions; loves Sophia and ultimately marries her.

Sophia Western

The heroine of the novel; motherless from the age of eleven; grows up into a remarkably beautiful and virtuous woman; sincerely loves Tom Jones and is willing to forgive his indiscretions; tries not to hurt her despotic father but is not unduly obsequious to him.

Blifil

The villain of the piece; in most respects the antithesis of Tom; selfish, malicious, hypocritical and thoroughly dishonest; fails to perform even a single honourable act in the course of the novel, hence appears to be unconvincing.

Squire Allworthy

Patron of Tom Jones; a benevolent wealthy widower; his purse is forever open to help those who are in distress; since he is prone to look upon all men as potentially good he is easily exploited by others; shows deplorable moral blindness in dismissing from his estate first Partridge and then Tom Jones; one of the weak characters of the novel.

Squire Western

Sophia's father; a typical country gentleman of Fielding's day; prude, boorish, hot-headed; hunting is his greatest love; takes great pleasure in the bottle; in politics he is a fool; his artistic tastes are low and vulgar; in domestic affairs he is a brutal tyrant; possesses a very vigorous speech; a highly comic character; supposed to be the single greatest creation in *Tom Jones.*

Mrs. Western

Sophia's aunt and Squire Western's sister; a self-opinionated woman; she prides herself on her knowledge of the world but continues to make blunders.

Mrs. Honour

Sophia's maid in the beginning of the novel; later takes up service with Lady Bellaston; vulgar, self-seeking, comical.

Benjamin Partridge

A poor schoolmaster; wrongly thought to be Tom's father; cowardly, superstitious, talkative but a faithful companion to Tom Jones almost till the end of the novel; a comic character portrayed in imitation of Cervante's Sancho Panza.

Jenny Jones (Mrs. Waters)

A servant woman, wrongly acknowledged Tom's mother; generous and noble-hearted but of easy-going virtue; plays a key role in the novel in revealing Tom's parentage at the end; ends up as the wife of Parson Supple.

Bridget Allworthy

Squire Allworthy's sister and the actual mother of Tom; mean, dishonest and hypocritical.

Captain Blifil

The husband of Bridget Allworthy; father of Blifil; greedy, selfish and disagreeable; betrays his brother Dr. Blifil who introduces him into the Allworthy family; contemptuous of his wife Bridget; dies two years after the marriage.

Dr. Blifil

An impoverished hanger-on at Allworthy's house; his only role in the novel is to introduce his brother Captain Blifil into the Allworthy family; later his brother treats him with gross ingratitude; he is compelled to leave the Allworthy estate for London, where he soon dies.

Thwackum

A minister of the Church of England; a tutor to Tom and Blifil; cruel and selfish, mean, vindictive and hypocritical; constantly quotes from the Scriptures to conceal his selfishness; like Blifil, whose favour he is always trying to win; does nothing good in the novel; ends up by alienating Allworthy by writing to him a harsh, self-seeking letter.

Square

Another hanger-on at Allworthy's house; a philosopher; Thwackum's constant adversary in a series of comic disputes; guilty of sexual hypocrisy; partly makes up for his earlier meanness by writing an atoning letter to Allworthy from his death bed.

Lady Bellaston

A thoroughly corrupt city woman; a widow or a divorcee; uses her wealth to seduce and keep a series of young men; she is so mean and unwomanly that she can propose to Lord Fellamar to rape Sophia and to plot Tom's impressment.

Lord Fellamar

Tries to rape Sophia at Lady Bellaston's residence in London; makes a plot to have Tom pressed into the navy; quite courageous for he is willing to fight a duel with Squire Western; is not irredeemably degenerated but makes an easy tool for Lady Bellaston's schemes.

Nightingale

A gay youngman about town; basically good at heart but weak of resolution; falls in love with Nancy Miller who gets pregnant by him; wants to marry Nancy but lacks courage to defy his materialistic father.

The elder Nightingale

A businessman of London; greedy and orthodox; selfish and materialistic; does not want his son Nightingale to marry Nancy.

Mrs. Miller

An innocent lady in London with whom Tom seeks lodgings when he goes there; Squire Allworthy also usually stays with her; plays an important role in the novel to get Tom reconciled to the Squire.

Nancy Miller

The daughter of Mrs. Miller; falls in love with Nightingale; Tom ultimately helps her to get married to him.

Mrs. Fitzpatrick

Sophia's cousin and the niece of Squire Western and Mrs. Western; attractive, self-willed and not particularly virtuous; wants to have an affair with Tom also but the latter ignores her hints; ends up by being a kept woman.

Mr. Fitzpatrick

An Irish adventurer, handsome but foolish and hot-headed; marries Mrs. Fitzpatrick and wastes most of her fortune; pursues her stubbornly when she runs away from him; picks up a pig-headed quarrel with Tom; makes Mrs. Waters his temporary wife.

Black George Seagrim

Allworthy's gamekeeper; dishonest; Tom helps him repeatedly but he pays with ingratitude; nevertheless performs a series of services to him, *e.g.* when Tom is in prison, he conveys his letter to Sophia; his dishonesty is perhaps due to his poverty and the large family he has to support.

Molly Seagrim

Black George's second daughter; attractive, seductive; seduces Tom but carries on an affair with the philosopher Square also; earlier has an affair with a young man Will Barnes by whom she gets pregnant; marries Partridge at the end of the novel.

Will Barnes

A young man, a local Don Juan who carries on an affair with Molly.

Dowling

The Salisbury attorney who brings the death bed message from Bridget; he acts as an aide to Blifil to all his schemes; his last action in the novel is to expose Blifil thoroughly to the angry Allworthy.

Arabella Hunt

A wealthy, attractive widow; proposes marriage to Tom when his fortunes are at a very low ebb; it is a respectable proposal but is, of course, rejected by Tom.

Deborah Wilkins

Squire Allworthy's housekeeper; old fashioned and hypocritical; it is she who brings the news that Jenny Jones is the mother of Tom.

Mrs. Partridge

The selfish, jealous, nagging wife of Partridge; a domineering woman; grossly misinterprets and misrepresents her husband's relations with Jenny Jones and is instrumental in his dismissal from the Allworthy estate.

The Man of the Hill

An old man whom Tom rescues from a band of ruffians; he has secluded himself from the society as a result of his bitter experiences; he is used to set off the positive aspect of Tom's outlook on life.

Parson Supple

Squire Western's chaplain; does not have any prominent role to play; marries Jenny Jones in the end.

Ensign Northerton

Is an ensign in the army; Tom quarrels with him when he gives an indecent remark when Tom proposes a toast to Sophia; promises to marry Jenny Jones but later tries to strangle her; Tom rescues Jenny from his clutches.

Captain Waters

The husband of Jenny Jones when she appears in the novel as Mrs. Waters.

Susan

The chamber-maid at the Upton Inn.

Summer

A young man who lived with Squire Allworthy for a shortwhile; the actual father of Tom; we never see him in person; that he is the father of Tom is revealed only at the end of the novel.

Anderson

A poor relative of Mrs. Miller who tries to rob Tom but is overpowered by the latters.

8

Characterisation in *Tom Jones*

Characters Drawn from Human Nature

In the introductory chapter to Book I, Fielding declares that his chief purpose in *Tom Jones* is the portrayal of *human nature.* He is fully conscious of the prodigious vastness and variety found in human nature, but he deems himself quite equal to the task. In *Tom Jones,* there are above forty characters, both major and minor, but all true representatives of human nature, all fully alive, all distinguished and individualised. Fielding depicts human nature faithfully and accurately; he neither embellishes nor idealises, neither extenuates nor conceals, neither exaggerates to caricature nor eschews to over-simplify, he depicts it as he observes it. He repeatedly claims, 'It is my business to relate matters of fact with veracity'; 'Our business is only to record truth', and in the course of the novel, he fully vindicates this claim. That is why Hazlitt thinks that as an observer of human nature, Fielding is 'little inferior to Shakespeare' and Byron remarks that 'Fielding is the prose Homer of human nature'.

Characters Neither Angelic Nor Diabolical But Real Human Beings

Since Fielding's characters are drawn according to nature, they are neither angels nor devils, neither paragons of virtue nor monsters of vice but real human beings compounded of both good and evil elements. If Tom is so easily vulnerable to sexual attraction, he is also chivalric and generous. Squire Western is no less indulgent than despotic, no less cowardly than hot-headed. Jenny Jones is artful and coquettish but is equally generous and open-hearted. All these characters have been conceived in their full complexity; they are both true to human nature and interesting—interesting, not essentially amiable or admirable, for some of them are definitely repulsive and contemptible—hence they have the capacity to fully engage the reader's mind. Two notable exceptions to this rule are the portrayals of Squire Allworthy and Blifil and both of them are wooden and rather uninteresting.

Characters Clearly Distinguished From One Another

There is no vagueness or indefiniteness about Fielding's characters. They are clearly distinguished. This is really remarkable in view of the very large number of characters portrayed by him. Even no two landladies are alike. This individuality is not realised through reiterating peculiar mannerisms of various characters—as is done by Smollett and more conspicuously, later by Dickens—but by carefully underlining the mass of traits that give a character its peculiar stamp. Dickens's characters are easy to remember on account of their tags—Uriah Heep has no eye-brows and hardly any eye lashes; Peggoty's blouse is always getting unbuttoned; Fagin the Jew has a very peculiar laughter to distinguish him—but such tags are rarely found in Fielding. Lady Bellaston has foul breath and Squire Western does have mannerism of speech, but we hardly know how Tom Jones or Blifil or Lord Fellamar or Nightingale looked like. And yet we know these characters so intimately that we can be hardly mistaken in identifying them.

Characters Transcribed From Real Life

Fielding usually models his characters after some one of his acquaintances. Squire Allworthy is drawn after his great friend and patron Ralph Allen of Bath. In Tom Jones, he has put much of himself. Sophia bears a very striking resemblance to his wife Charlotte Cradock. His model for Squire Western is the Tory sportsman, Mildmay, the great friend of Pope and Bolingbroke. But Fielding does not just transcribe. With the lone exception of Sophia who approximates most closely to Fielding's late wife, all the characters in the novel draw from both observation and invention. He takes real-life models but fuses fact and fancy and adapts them to the needs of the novel. He recombines the traits, exaggerates here, moderates there, sometimes heightens an idiosyncrasy, sometimes tones it down, and produces a character highly original. In this respect, in his Preface to *Joseph Andrews,* he remarks:

> For though everything is copied from the book of nature, and scarce a character or action produced which I have not taken from my own observations and experiences: yet I have used the utmost care to obscure the persons by such different circumstances, degrees and colours, that it will be impossible to guess at them with any degree of certainty.

Characters Contrasted With One Another

A perceptive reader can easily discern that Fielding's characters gain prominence through being contrasted with one another. Tom's virtuousness is set off by Blifil's wickedness; his courage and sense of responsibility, by Nightingale's cowardliness; and the positiveness of his approach to life, by the negation of life we find in the Man of-the Hill. Similarly through contrast first with Molly, then with Mrs. Fitzpatrick, and finally with Lady Bellaston, the appeal of Sophia's feminine grace, her innate virtue and her fidelity in love is definitely enhanced. The contrast between Allworthy's cool-headedness and Western's rashness in the first few books is quite obvious. But sometimes apparent contrasts conceal fine ironic parallelisms—Thwackum and Square hold divergent views but both are great hypocrites. With Fielding, however, this method of contrasting characters is not complete as with Thackeray, who conceives characters almost in pairs. In *Tom Jones,* contrasts are suggested by similarity of situation.

No Psychological Analysis of Characters

In the delineation of his characters, Fielding usually makes no attempt at any minute psychological analysis in the manner of Richardson. This, however, does not imply that his knowledge of human nature is inferior to that of Richardson, or as Dr. Johnson believes, that Fielding is contented with 'the husk of life' while Richardson is concerned with the 'kernal', or that Fielding being a 'superficial observer' draws only 'characters of manners' while Richardson being capable of diving into 'the recesses of the human heart, portrays characters of nature'. The fact is that Fielding's characters are as much distinct individuals, 'characters of nature" as those of Richardson. Only, the two great masters differ in their mode of delineation. Fielding has essentially a comic vision, and a writer of comedies has to avoid the analytical method, while the impact of tragedy gets intensified through an analysis of the inner conflicts. Secondly, while Richardson reveals his understanding of the recesses of human consciousness by means of diaries and letters which are in reality soliloquies, Fielding reveals it by means of dialogue. Richardson is analytical, Fielding is dramatic. However, when Fielding chooses to analyse, he is not incapable of it; for example, he depicts quite convincingly the conflict between avarice and conscience in the heart of Black George on the question of purloining Sophia's purse of sixteen guineas.

Characters and Incidents Harmonised

Fielding strikes an ideal harmony between the character and the incident. The incidents are shaped by the characters. One of the earliest complicating actions in the novel is the withholding of Bridget's secret by Blifil. This is strictly in concord with Blifil's malicious nature. Tom's dismissal from the Allworthy household accords with his godfather's moral blindness we have seen earlier as well. Similarly the incidents at the Upton Inn follow from the characters of the protagonists. In their turn, the characters are moulded and revealed by the incidents. Tom, for example, learns from his earlier sexual involvements and develops emotional maturity and stability before winning Sophia's hand in marriage.

Lifelike Portraits of Children

Fielding is the first English novelist to introduce lifelike portraits of children in his novels. The portraits of Tom and Blifil in their early childhood are sheer artistic triumphs. The stirring of the first emotions of love, the gradual awakening of the innocent child into the artful, amorous world of the adult is beautifully depicted in Sophia and Tom. Similarly the natural yearnings of a healthy lad unrestrained by any social or moral ethos are beautifully depicted in Tom Jones.

Characters Both Local and Universal

As pointed out earlier, Fielding has real life characters as most of his models. His characters are the true representatives of the eighteenth century society. In fact Fielding is the true historian of the eighteenth century manners and *Tom Jones* is a great epic of the eighteenth century England. Allworthy and Western, Partridge and Jenny Jones, Thwackum and Square, Lady Bellaston and Lord Fellamar are all typical eighteenth century products. But underlying their local and temporal forms, these characters also reveal the true universal nature. They are the hypocrites, the gallants, the debauches one can find anywhere. These characters are local as well as universal, individual as well as types, that is their beauty.

No Caricatures

Fielding usually avoids caricaturisation. He does have a perceptive eye for eccentric and comic traits and takes delight in depicting them. Occasionally he heightens them also. The peculiarities of Mrs. Western and Parson Thwackum are obviously heightened and intensified. But this is at best accentuation and not distortion. It does not stagger our belief in the substantial truth of these characters. The one great master in the art of caricaturisation is Dickens; his characters—Mr. Micawber, Mrs. Gamp, Mr. Pecksniff—catch the reader's eye. But they are flat, in E.M. Forster's sense of the word. They are incapable of surprising us. Caricatures may amuse, but they cannot surprise, for they cannot develop. Many characters in *Tom Jones* are episodic and make only short appearances but we get the feeling that there is more to them than we see.

Characters Mostly From Lower and Middle Classes. Characters Only Homely and Pedestrian

It has been pointed out that Fielding's world is mainly the world of middle and lower classes. A Lord Fellamar or a Lady Bellaston makes only a rare appearance. Fielding usually avoids depicting members of the aristocratic classes. The aristocracy was perhaps a little too artificial and conventionalised to arouse genuine interest in an imaginative writer, Secondly, Fielding understands best only homely and pedestrian men and women. One of the eminent critics points out:

> He (Fielding) could not understand either a great saint or a great sinner. He had no comprehension of spiritual fervour or exaltation, which he would have deemed mere ebullition of hypocrisy or folly; nor, on the other hand, did he really plumb the abysses of the reprobate and abandoned soul Ordinary human nature, not exceptionally glorified nor exceptionally debased, was the subject of his investigation; the extraordinary potentialities of humanity for good and evil were not taken into account in his philosophy.

9

Major Characters

TOM JONES

Parentage, Physical Features

Tom Jones, the hero of the novel, is born of a handsome youngman Summer, who stays at the Allworthy estate for some time and Miss Bridget, the Squire's sister. But his parentage is revealed only towards the end of the novel. Squire Allworthy regards him as Jenny Jones's son begotten by Partridge—hence his name *Tom Jones*—while most of the people, including Partridge, think him to be Squire Allworthy's illegitimate son. He grows up into a well-formed, handsome personality with comely features. He has effeminate grace but masculine ruggedness. Fielding invests him with the beauty of Adonis and the strength of Hercules. Besides, he is 'a robust youngman—a tireless walker, a fearless rider and a boxer in strength and agility almost a match for a professional'. There is every reason to believe that he is cast in the likeness of Fielding himself.

Brought Up As a Bastard

Tom is brought up with the stigma of being a bastard indelibly stamped on him. Despite Bridget's preferential treatment, he receives scant respect and affection. Blifil loses no opportunity of vilifying his character and with the scheming Square and Thwackum ever with Blifil, Tom finds no one to receive him cordially. Squire Allworthy, with all his sense of justice, fails to see through the designs of the contriving trio and remains stiff, indifferent, inaccessible. So Tom has to keep company with the dishonest Black George and the despotic and rash Squire Western. It is both astonishing and praiseworthy that in spite of such unfavourable circumstances, Tom grows up into a very healthy youngman, free from any mental complexes and retains the innate goodness of heart. By giving an exactly identical parentage and the same domestic circumstances to both Tom and Blifil, perhaps it was Fielding's aim to affirm that character is innate rather than cultivated.

Goodness of Heart

The dominating quality of Tom, as pointed out by Dudden, is the goodness of heart:

> ......this good-heartedness meant precisely two things—first, a readiness to do a kindness whenever an opportunity offered, and secondly, a determination to inflict no injury on anyone if he could help it.

And Tom is willing to help others even at the risk of his own life. Thus he rushes to Sophia's help when she is thrown off the horse, and breaks his own arm to retrieve the bird she so dearly loved. He saves the Man of the Hill from the ruffians who had waylaid him to rob him of his belongings, and the very next morning he overpowers Northerton to save Mrs. Waters from being strangled. If in helping others, he has to take recourse to a lie, he does not hesitate and lies with tenacity. He lies to Squire Allworthy that he alone was involved in the poaching incident and stubbornly adheres to the lie. But he lies to save Black George, not himself. While making an estimate of his character on the basis of his involvement in these incidents, due importance must be given to his motives. He lies to Lady Bellaston when he proposes marriage to her. But he has no eye on her property; he lies to disengage himself from her detestable amorous advances. He lies to the elder Nightingale when he tells him that Nancy and Nightingale are already married. But he lies to secure the happiness of the young couple.

Tom never consciously hurts anyone. In Book XIV chapter 4, he says to Nightingale:

> I am no canting hypocrite, nor do I pretend to the gift of chastity. I have been guilty with women, I own it; but am not conscious I have injured any; nor would I, to procure pleasure to myself, be knowingly the cause of misery to any human being.

On the contrary, even when others hurt him, he is willing to forgive and forget. He forgives the highwayman for having attacked him, and moved by his pathetic tale, he even offers him two guineas from his slender allowance. He pleads to Squire Allworthy to forgive Black George in view of the irresistibility of the temptation the poor gamekeeper had to face when he came by the five hundred pound bill Allworthy had presented to Tom. He even requests his godfather to forgive Blifil though he has suffered a lifetime of torture on account of his wickedness and treachery. When Tom proposes to his uncle to forgive Blifil, Mrs. Miller is forced to remark, "You are too good, Mr. Jones, infinitely too good to live in this world." Even Squire Allworthy whose generosity is celebrated all over his estate stands no match to Tom. While forgiving Black George, the Squire comments, "Child, you carry this forgiving temper too far. Such mistaken mercy is not only weakness but borders on injustice and is very pernicious to society, as it encourages vice. The dishonesty of this fellow I might perhaps have pardoned, but never his ingratitude." The Squire cannot be persuaded to see the face of Blifil again, but Tom goes to the extent of secretly adding to the two hundred pounds a year settled on him by Squire Allworthy.

Affection for Squire Allworthy

Tom's affection for Squire Allworthy and his sense of gratitude to him are also praise-worthy. Although he is subjected to a great deal of inconvenience on account of the moral blindness of his godfather, he never utters a word of protest, nor does he tolerate a word of complaint against him. He is the only one genuinely afflicted when Squire Allworthy falls ill and truly relieved and delighted to get the news that he is out of danger. The philosopher Square's testimony from his deathbed is very relevant here:

> Believe me, my dear friend, when I tell you on the word of a dying man, he (Tom) hath been basely injured...When you lay upon your supposed deathbed, he was the only person in the house who testified any real concern; and what happened afterwards arose from the wildness of his joy on your recovery; ...He hath some faults, but among them is not to be numbered the least want of duty or gratitude towards you. On the contrary, I am satisfied, when you dismissed him from your house, his heart bled for you more than for himself.

Sexual Liaisons

Tom has often been condemned for his liaisons with various women, but it is significant to observe that in all the three cases—Molly, Mrs. Waters and Lady Bellaston—he is the seduced rather than the seducer and each of these affairs is attended by attenuating circumstances. In the case of Molly, there is a very clear indication that the affair is initiated by her, and Tom, once he realises that he desires her, resists her for three months before eventually succumbing to her coquetry. A simpleton as he is, he is duped into believing that it is he who has seduced Molly and fathered the child being carried by her, and despite his gradual awareness of his love for Sophia, he treats Molly with complete honesty and generosity. He tries to suppress his instinctive love for Sophia and does not acknowledge it openly till it is disclosed that the child in Molly's womb is probably not of Tom at all, but that of Will Barnes, Molly's first lover.

Tom goes to bed with Mrs. Waters at the Upton Inn. Here again, Tom is seduced. Mrs. Waters makes her designs clear in the very beginning when she persistently refuses to cover her exposed breasts as Tom leads her from the site of the incident to the Upton Inn. His adversary is much older than he himself is and is highly experienced in sexual ethics; at the Upton inn, while Tom is fully absorbed in his dinner, she deliberately brings to bear 'the whole artillery of love' and 'every engine of amorous warfare' till Tom is subdued and he retires to her bed.

Finally, there is his affair with Lady Bellaston. He does allow himself to be debauched by the Lady. But there is a complex web of circumstances in which Tom finds himself entangled and which have to be carefully analysed before any judgment can be passed on him. First of all, Tom 'had never less inclination to an amour 'than on that evening, but he is afraid to offend a person who has it in her power to put him in touch with Sophia. Secondly, 'gallantry to the ladies was among his principles of honour' and 'he held it as much incumbent on him to accept a challenge to love as if it had been a challenge to fight'. Thirdly, he has absolutely no money. We know Partridge had lent him money to pay for his conveyance to the masquerade and from there to Lady Bellaston's lodgings, he has to walk on foot. Thus the temptation to accept Lady Bellaston's gift of £50 is quite irresistible, but he offers the whole of this money to Mrs. Miller to relieve the distress of the Andersons. He continues the relation with the Lady; rather, it should be said that he continues to suffer the foul breath of the Lady but has a very strange logic to offer. "He knew the consideration upon which all her favours were conferred," says Fielding, "and as his necessity obliged him to accept them, so his honour, he concluded, forced him to pay the price."

But having said this, all has not been said about Tom's amorous affairs. When at the dining table at Sophia's, Tom learns that Molly is likely to be punished and he abruptly rises from the table, howsoever vaguely it might be, he must have sensed he has caused pain to Sophia. He is still guilty of indiscretion when in Book V, he retreats into a thicket with Molly. Only a few moments before Molly's appearance, Tom was thinking of Sophia:

> O Sophia, would heaven give thee to my arms, how blest would be my condition ! Oh ! my fond heart is so wrapped in that tender bosom that the brightest beauties would for me have no charms, nor would a hermit be colder in their embraces. Sophia, Sophia alone shall be mine.

Gradually Develops Discretion

But a minute later Molly appears and Tom has his rendezvous. In spite of the extenuating factors present here—Tom's drunkenness and the absence of any hope of winning Sophia—Fielding is clearly satirical of Tom's indulgence. Tom learns a lesson at the Upton inn, where, had he not been loose with Mrs. Waters, he would not have lost Sophia. There is no end to his chagrin as he notices Sophia's muff in his bed. He falls into self-condemnation but later again succumbs to Lady Bellaston. His motivation apart, his proposal to Lady Bellaston destroys all his hopes of winning Sophia and he must have rued the entire affair. He realises that he must resist all carnal temptations if he is to be worthy of Sophia's hand. Very politely but determinedly he turns down the widow Arabella Hunt's proposal, and with as much restraint, he ignores the hints thrown by Mrs. Fitzpatrick. Ultimately he does learn that the needs of the flesh may be quite normal, and even pressing, but they have to be indulged in with discretion.

Lives by Impulse

Tom always lives by impulse, not by reason—and his impulses are not trained. He has naturally boisterous animal spirits that lead him to extravagances. When delighted, or grieved, or angry, or anxious, he is apt to fall into paroxysms of frenzied excitement and to behave literally like a mad man. In the beginning, he has a volatile and unbalanced temperament and his mind works with a very strange logic. He does not touch Sophia's banknote but accepts £50 from Lady Bellaston and on another impulse, he offers the entire amount to Mrs. Miller. He overpowers the highwayman but on learning his distress offers him money. Critics have accused him of possessing a disordered mind, but isn't there a streak of reason in his madness ?

His impulses, being indisciplined, lead him into disgraceful digressions in the beginning, but the same impulses brought under control and discreetly channelised set off his virtues.

Tom and Blifil

The goodness of Tom's heart is made amply clear by contrasting him with Blifil, the Man of the Hill and Nightingale. Tom is impulsively generous; Blifil is selfish and scheming. Blifil's ostentatious display of virtue covers the vilest meanness; Tom's most blatant indulgences are induced by noble instincts. The brief incident relating to Sophia's bird clearly presents the contrast. Blifil cajoles Sophia into giving him the bird for a moment and then releases it, his argument being, 'I always thought there was something very cruel in confining anything. It seemed to be against the law of nature, by which everything has a right to liberty; nay it is even unchristian'. But the fact is that Blifil is jealous of Tom and he instinctively resents the pleasure Sophia derives from Tom's present. Tom, in his effort to retrieve the bird, falls into the canal. Squire Western, crude as he is, gives very apt comments on the conduct of both Tom and Blifil. About Tom, he says, "...to venture breaking his neck to oblige my girl was a generous spirited action; I have learning enough to see that," and about Blifil, his verdict is that "if Blifil were his son, his backside should be well flea'd."

Tom and Man of the Hill

Contrast with the Man of the Hill brings out the sanity of Tom's attitude towards life. Both Tom Jones and the Man of the Hill have been wronged by society but the former has withdrawn from human society and has come to believe that 'human nature is everywhere the same, everywhere the object of detestation and scorn'. Tom has even greater reason to condemn human nature, but he has not turned a sceptic or a cynic. The Man of the Hill disgraces the potential dignity of man; Tom Jones upholds it. But for Tom's timely intervention, the old man would have fallen a helpless victim to the ruffians, yet the very next morning, when Tom repeats his action, this time to rescue Mrs. Waters, the old man tries to check him.

Tom and Nightingale

And finally, Nightingale is exactly in the same situation in which once Tom had found himself. Nancy is pregnant, and it is clearly stated that Nightingale had promised her marriage while seducing her. Still he is willing to concede to his father's wishes to marry a rich girl. Tom had never given any such promise to Molly, still Tom boldly owns his supposed responsibility to her.

SOPHIA

Fascinating Personality

Sophia Western, partly modelled after Fielding's first wife Charlotte Cradock, is undoubtedly the finest character in the novel. Motherless from the age of eleven, she has been brought up by her aunt Mrs. Western and is about eighteen when she is first introduced to us. She is a middle-sized woman, but rather inclining to tall. Her shape is not only exact but extremely delicate. Her luxuriant hair fashionably cut and gracefully curled on her neck, her lustrous black eyes, her oval cheeks with a dimple in the right cheek which the least smile discovers, her lily-white complexion that turns vermilion with a little modesty or exercise—all these give her a fascinatingly beautiful personality.

Sweet-tempered; Refined in Manners

Sophia's mind is, in every way, equal to her person; rather, the latter borrows some charm from the former; for 'when she smiled, the sweetness of her temper diffused that glory over her countenance, which no regularity of features can give'. Since her aunt is a lady of great discretion, and is thoroughly acquainted with the world, having lived in her youth about the Court, under her guidance, whatever mental accomplishments Sophia has derived from nature are improved and cultivated by art. She lacks 'a little of that ease in her behaviour, which is to be acquired only by habit, and living within what is called the polite circle', but we need not feel sorry, says Fielding, for 'its absence is well compensated by innocence; nor can good sense, and a natural gentility ever stand in need of it'.

Devoted to Her Father, Courageous

Sophia is devoted to her father and does not want to hurt him at any cost. Her filial piety is almost religious in temper. In Book XVI, chapter 2, she says to her father, "may heaven blast me if there is a misery I would not suffer to preserve you." Squire Western is a coarse and brutal drunkard who would even like to prevent her from cherishing the memory of her mother. Still she loves him and in almost everything accepts his word as law. She has a fondness only for the soft music of Handel, but in order to gratify her father's crude taste, she repeatedly plays his favourite jigs upon her harpsichord. Hunting can be no sport for a delicate woman like Sophia, but in order to please her father, she accompanies him on his hunting sprees whenever she can. It is in the course of such a hunting expedition that she is thrown off her horse, and Tom, trying to save her, breaks his arm. However, on one point she does not concede to the dictatorial wishes of her father. She loathes Blifil and cannot be forced into acquiescence to accept him as her life partner. She can promise not to marry anyone without her father's full consent, but she cannot give in to his tyrannical threats if his desires go against her inclinations. It needs extreme courage to leave the security of her father's house at the dead of night and to face the perils of the country roads, but Sophia is amply possessed of such courage. Under the delicate veneer of this doll-like 'little darling' of her father, there throbs a heart far more hardy and courageous than the one possessed by the feeble women of her age. She remains undaunted by the threat of the roadside dangers and inconveniences and as they are preparing themselves for the escape, she says to her maid, "A good brisk pace will preserve us from the cold and if you cannot defend me from a villain, Honour, I will defend you for I will take a pistol with me." This is no idle a claim, for in Book X, chapter 9, when a man rides up to her in the darkness, 'she neither screamed out nor fainted away'. And there is such a radiance of virtue on her face that as she journeys from inn to inn, the inmates everywhere hold her in respect and awe and no sexual levity is attached to her anywhere.

Love with Tom: Constancy and Magnanimity

In her love with Tom, Sophia displays courage, magnanimity and consistent fidelity. "It took some courage to contemplate union with a man whom almost everyone spoke ill of. And it needed no little magnanimity to forgive his numerous shortcomings," says Dudden. Sophia had fallen in love with Tom without realising it. The first awareness of her growing passion for Tom she gets through a very painful experience. On hearing the news that Molly Seagrim is in distress, Tom abruptly leaves the dining table at Squire Western's and rushes to meet Squire Allworthy, and Sophia suffers a pang. This first awareness of love is very painful and it augurs ill for the lovers. Tom is a branded bastard, with no social status, no expectations, nobody to speak well of. Still, Sophia recognises his amiable qualities, his bravery, generosity, high-spiritedness, chivalry, innate goodness of heart and ingenuity, and acknowledges her love for Tom. Apart from courage, it needs magnanimity to forgive his undesirable liaisons with women. She forgives him not only for his affair with Molly but even helps Molly with clothes. Sir is willing even to overlook his involvement with Mrs. Waters at the Upton Inn. What offends her most is the fact that her name is freely bandied up and down the country inns, though the poor girl is unaware that it is usually Partridge and not Tom who is responsible for it. Later she feels offended by Tom's proposal of marriage to Lady Bellaston 'at the very time when you would have me imagine you were under such concern on my account'. Somehow nothing appears to be winning her back, neither the persuasion of Squire Allworthy nor the pleadings of Squire Western, nor even the explanation offered by Mrs. Miller. Only when she is thoroughly convinced of Tom's fidelity, does she ultimately give her consent for marriage.

Rejection of Blifil

Sophia's fidelity in love is evident from her two rejections of very desirable-looking matrimonial alliances, one with Blifil and the other with Lord Fellamar. And there are domestic pressures to accept either of them. Blifil, the heir-apparent to the Allworthy estate is, on the surface at least, a man without any moral blemish; his conduct looks irreproachable, and his moral virtues are so highly played up by his tutors Thwackum and Square. But Sophia with an intuitive perception of Blifil's hypocrisy and his abject baseness, feels repugnance for him, and having once rejected him, never agrees to revise her decision. Not even her father's threats that he would disinherit her and turn her out of his house stark naked make any impact on her mind. Towards the end of the book, Squire Western again pleads with her to accept Blifil and put an end to his troubles, but Sophia does not yield.

Rejection of Lord Fellamar

Alliance with Lord Fellamar could herald her entrance into nobility. Lord Fellamar is a handsome nobleman whose behaviour before and after the attempted rape on Sophia from which she is so opportunely rescued by Squire Western merits no censure. And Sophia's aunt Mrs. Western is simply fascinated with the proposal. It needs great constancy of mind to resist the offer of Lord Fellamar and accept a base foundling like Tom Jones.

Not too Perfect to Look Human

Fortunately Sophia is not drawn too perfect to look human. She is capable of clever flattery. When Mrs. Western is forcing her to marry Lord Fellamar, Sophia flatters her to compunction and the impending calamity is averted for the time being. This is not deceit or dishonesty; this is simply womanlike ingeniousness which she employs to extricate herself from an impossible situation. She also has a little vanity which, though for a fleeting moment, makes her toy with the idea of sacrificing herself to filial piety and be a martyr, the type of vanity one encounters in an imbecile, invertebrate heroine like Thackeray's Amelia. But Sophia is definitely healthier and more wholesome, and her natural responses to her situation are more human. Her flaws simply humanise her; they do not lower her in our esteem.

SQUIRE ALLWORTHY

Meant To Be An Embodiment of Goodness

Squire Allworthy, as his name suggests, has been depicted as an essentially good man. Keeping before him his friend and patron, Ralph Allen of Bath, Fielding has in fact, tried to portray Squire Allworthy as the very incarnation of goodness. He is moved to tears at the slightest provocation, is 'replete with beneficence' and is 'ever ready to relieve the distress of others'. He settles an annuity on Mrs. Miller. He gives Tom £500 to enable him to earn an honest livelihood even as he banishes him from his estate. And like a true Christian, he contrives 'on all occasions to hide his beneficence not only from the world but from the object of it'. No wonder people refer to him as 'that good man', 'this worthy man'.

Credulous, Morally blind, Lacks Insight

But having said this, we have said all that could be said in his praise.

In Book VII, chapter 3, Fielding tells us that Squire Allworthy was 'as great a pattern...of true wisdom...as he was of goodness'. But it is doubtful whether he is quite a satisfactory or convincing pattern. On the contrary, he lacks sagacity and when he is most complacently confident of his judgment, he is most pitiably mistaken, and instead of meeting out justice, he subjects people to gross injustice and does definite harm to them. His credulity is exploited and he is duped; his generosity is reviled and he is maligned. He misunderstands and is misunderstood. Those who benefit from his charity hardly deserve it; those who deserve kindliness are treated rather cruelly. Thus he banishes both Tom Jones and Partridge from the Allworthy estate though both of them are innocent. He shelters the Blifil brothers, the doctor and the captain, and approves of a marriage that brings nothing but misery to his sister. He harbours in his household the philosopher Square and divine Thwackurn who are both loathsome hypocrites. He fails to discern the diabolical treachery of Blifil beneath the veneer of piety and solemnity, or the natural goodness of Tom concealed by his frivolity and boisterousness. He owns the one, banishes the other, and betrays a grave lack of perspicacity. Perhaps Fielding is aware of the Squire's inadequacy as a convincing character; hence he often tries to defend him. At times, Fielding endows him with a vague awareness of the reality. We are told that he has his 'doubts' about Thwackum. Or when the doctor tries to prepare a background to disclose his brother's romance with Miss Bridget, he discovers that Allworthy has already made a note of it and approves of the marriage. But this awareness of the reality is too feeble and vague to defend him. On another occasion, Fielding, in order to defend the Squire argues that if any of his readers were in his position, he would be equally deceived by Thwackum. If the reader now knows better, and feels like censuring the Squire's lack of penetrativeness, it is because the author has taken him into confidence and shared with him his knowledge of the parson's malicious and mischievous Nature:

> ...for the reader is greatly mistaken if he conceives that Thwackum appeared to Mr. Allworthy in the same light as he doth to him in the history; and he is as much deceived, if he imagines that the most intimate acquaintance which he himself could have had with that divine, would have informed him of those things which we, from our inspiration are enabled to open and discover.

There is yet a third argument offered by Fielding in defence of Allworthy. Though he often questions the justness and regularity of Allworthy's conduct, for example when he decides to commit Molly to Bridewell, the house of correction, he never questions his motives:

> However, as his intention was truly upright, he ought to be excused in *foro conscientiae;* since so many arbitrary acts are daily committed by magistrates who have not this excuse to plead for themselves.

Fielding wanted us to judge Tom Jones by his motives, his intentions, and not merely by his actions, and the same criterion we ought to apply to the Squire as well.

Deficient in Passion and Humour; Stiff and Wooden

In addition to this lack of insight, Squire Allworthy is miserably deficient in passion. 'It was Mr. Allworthy's custom', Fielding tells us, 'never to punish anyone, not even to turn away a servant in a passion'. He displays the same lack of passion when Squire Western brings to him the proposal of marriage between Blifil and Sophia. Allworthy receives Mr. Western's proposal without any visible emotion, or without any alteration of countenance, and the warm blooded Western is frankly irritated. Normally Fielding does not approve of a "person who knows how to subdue appetites and passion, for such a person must be a hypocrite, and he warns his readers to beware of him. But he is not in the least ironical or critical when he portrays Squire Allworthy as deficient in passion and he wants us to admire his cool-headedness (and cold-heartedness ?). Squire Allworthy lacks humour too and he takes himself as well as everybody else with solemn seriousness. Consequently, in him, we get a character that is too dull and unintelligent, too stiff and wooden, too cold and flat, to be altogether admirable. It is surprising how Fielding expected his patron Ralph Allen to be pleased with this portrayal of his or how he expected his readers to accept Squire Allworthy as an ideal of human excellence or as 'the glory of the human species 'and to respect him. Squire Allworthy's character is definitely one of the weaknesses of *Tom Jones.*

SQUIRE WESTERN

Vitally Alive

Squire Western is perhaps the most alive, the most original character in *Tom Jones.* He is a specimen of the ignorant, hard-drinking, Tory landowner half a century behind the times. His delineation has been appreciated by critics and readers alike for two centuries and he must have held great fascination fo, his creator, for he has made persistent appearances in Fielding's earlier dramatic works, as Sir Positive Trap in *Love in Several Masques* and as Squire Badger in *Don Quixote in England.* His original model most probably was Carew Hervey Mildmay—Horace Walpole's 'old Mildmay, whose lungs and memory, and tongue, will never wear out', but it is also likely that while delineating Squire Western, Fielding did not confine himself to any single model but drew hints from a number of other country gentlemen whom he had met in his 'hunting excursions in Somerset and Dorset. About Squire Western, one of the French contemporaries of Fielding remarks:

> I do not know that English literature has produced any other figure as full of life as this country Squire whose sallies, freaks, unreasonableness, obstinacy, coarseness, roughness, brutal kindness, and love of sport and the bottle, make up as arrant a country gentleman as ever walked the country of Somerset. He is nearly always in the wrong but

> with the best faith in the world, and it is real pleasure to listen to him.

A Typical Country Squire

Squire Western has been portrayed as a typical country Squire His thoughts and interests are centred either in the field, the stable or the dog kennel ! In the mornings he is engaged with hunting or some other violent outdoor exercise; after his two o'clock dinner he passes his time in deep potations with some boon companion; and when he goes to bed, he is generally so drunk, he cannot see. He dabbles with politics only to betray his foolishness, for he favours, the return of the Stuarts to the English throne. He is a justice of the peace, but he miserably lacks the knowledge of the laws he is supposed to administer. His taste in music is vulgar and crude, for he shows fondness only for a few old country airs while Sophia swears by Handel.

Irrational and Unreasonable

Squire Western is a most irrational, unreasonable type of man. Fielding tells us that 'he had not the least command over his passions'. He falls into violent fits of passion over mere trifles. When Tom Jones and Black George shoot a partridge on his estate, he raves and rants 'in as high terms and as bitter language as if his house had been broken open, and the most valuable furniture stole out of it'. In his general conduct, he is usually inconsiderate and at times brutal and barbarous. While his wife is alive, he treats her with scant respect and does not even conceal his hatred for her. But the pity is that even after her death, he does not spare her:

> ....when anything in the least soured him, as a bad scenting day, or a distemper among His hounds, or any other such misfortune, he constantly vented his spleen by invectives against the deceased, saying 'if my wife was alive now, she would be glad of this'.

Sophia who dearly loved her mother must have felt hurt at this insensitive treatment of her mother.

Despotic Father

As a father, Squire Western is most despotic and dictatorial. He is quite indulgent with Sophia but is most unreasonably intolerant of even the least deviation from his wishes. His authoritarian attitude verges on the ridiculous. When he is acquainted with Sophia's being in love, he is immediately infuriated:

> How ! in love ! in love without acquainting me ! I'll disinherit her; I'll turn her out of doors, stark naked, without a farthing.

When Mrs. Western tells him that Sophia might be in love with the very person he might approve of, he says:

> If she marries the man I would have her, she may love whom she pleases.

Later when he comes to know that she is in love with Tom Jones and not Blifil, he is again mad with fury. All of Sophia's implorings and entreaties fail to touch his heart and draw only a scornful remark:

> Pooh pooh ! ....all stuff and nonsense; all maidenish tricks; I am resolved upon the match.

Then he pleads with her:

> I tell thee, it will preserve me; it will give me health, happiness, life, everything. Upon my soul, I shall die if dost refuse me; I shall break my heart, I shall, upon my soul.

When she still resists, he clenches his fist, bites his lips and declares that even though she hangs herself the next morning, this marriage *shall* take place. This smacks of a childish rashness and impetuosity. His responses are impulsive; his impulses are unrefined and unrestrained. That is why his landlady considers him 'a very *hastish* kind of a gentleman', his sister calls him 'absolutely a perfect *Groat*' and Lady Bellaston declares him a *Hottentot.*

Respects Only Materialistic Values

Squire Western's treatment of Sophia shows him both as a traditional father with unflinching faith in parental authority and a shrewd eighteenth century landlord with respect only for materialistic values. If he is so insistent that Sophia marries Blifil, it is as much because he brooks no defiance of parental authority as because he deems it prudent to have a matrimonial alliance with the wealthy and respectable Allworthy family. In Book VII, the same Squire Western berates his sister in the most unkind terms, only a moment later, on being reminded of her immense fortune, meekly surrenders to her and persuades her to return. Doesn't it show that the Squire, even in his most violent fits of passion, never loses sight of what can bestow on him any material benefits ?

Basically a Weak Man

In spite of the elements of crudity and violence in Squire Western's temper, he is basically a weak character. He confesses to Allworthy the vulnerability of his nature:

> I do not know how 'tis, but d—n me, Allworthy, if you do not make me always do just as you please.

And in his encounter with Captain Egglane in London, he gets real panicky and betrays a degree of cowardice that appears to be inconsistent with his character as a country squire.

His Portrayal is Very Successful

But on the whole, his character breathes vitality. In contrast with him, Squire Allworthy looks dull and wooden. Since we laugh at him, we do not feel horrified. To a certain extent, we even like him, for in his own rough way, he is capable of kindness, and his love for Sophia, howsoever irrational, is quite genuine. But the secret of Fielding's success with him lies in the vigorous speech he endows him with.

BLIFIL

The Villain of the Novel

Blifil, the son of Captain Blifil and Bridget, is the villain of the novel. He seems to have inherited a veraciousness and treachery, dishonesty and meanness from his parents and engrained these qualities in his character by assiduous pursuit. An arrant knave, a very devil incarnate, he is the most detestable character in the novel, his villainy being unmitigated by even a single redeeming action. He is almost a typed character, like the vice or the devil taken directly out of the morality plays. He is not very different from Moliere's Tartuffe though in the absence of any plausible motives for villainy, he is less convincing than Tartuffe.

Mask of Piety and Solemnity

In the beginning, Blifil is presented to us as 'a lad of remarkable disposition; sober, discreet and pious beyond his age'. His mask of piety and solemnity wins him the favour of Squire Allworthy, while with carefully worn respectfulness and adroit flattery, he ingratiates himself to his tutors, Thwackum and Square. Fielding beautifully describes his method:

> With one he was all religion, with the other he was all virtue. And when both were present, he was profoundly silent, which both interpreted in his favour and in their own.

Malicious and Hypocritical

Blifil is both malicious and hypocritical. He maligns and hurts others simply for the pleasure of it, but he knows how to ascribe his vilest actions to the purest motives. He releases Sophia's bird simply to hurt Sophia and Tom, but he offers a very specious excuse:

> I had Miss Sophia's bird in my hand, and thinking the poor creature languished for liberty, I own, I could not forbear giving it what it desired; for I always thought there was something very cruel in confining anything. It seemed to be against the law of nature, by which everything has a right to liberty; nay, it is even unchristian, for it is not doing what we would be done by.

He seeks to hasten the end of his sick uncle by giving him the bad news of his mother's death. He is resolved to communicate this news to his uncle in defiance of the physician's instructions, but has again a very convincing excuse to offer: ".......if his uncle recovered.......he knew he would never forgive an endeavour to keep a secret of this kind from him." He is bent on marrying Sophia, for he covets both her fortune and her person, but more than that, he wants to wreak vengeance on Sophia for her partiality for Tom and on Tom for having had the privilege of being loved by Sophia. But with grave solemnity, he declares that he has accepted the role of Sophia's betrothed with a view to weaning her heart from the wretched Jones who is bound to make her miserable. One wonders what pious excuse he would have offered to cover up his conspiracy towards the end of the novel to get Tom exiled or convicted of murder.

His Courtship of Sophia

Blifil's courtship of Sophia presents him as a heinous character. In a way he is comparable to the insufferable Solmes who makes awkward and repugnant advances to Clarissa; simply, he is more unscrupulous, more malevolent than Solmes, and is more formidable. He has affinities with Lovelace also, who torments Clarissa for his personal pleasure because she is virtuous and he does not believe in virtue. Blifil is more stiff and theoretical than Lovelace; but he is more potentially dangerous than his notorious contemporary. Fielding, in no mistakable terms, establishes that the real source of danger to virtue and innocence is not an outspoken rake and lecher like Lovelace but an oily tongued hypocrite like Blifil.

Not Very Subtle; Except Allworthy, Nobody is Deceived by Him

It is interesting to notice that Fielding has given Blifil no Christian name. He is invariably called Blifil—and this seems to be a variation of Bluff-all. Blifil is really a big fraud and he does try to bluff every body in the novel. But his efforts are a dismal failure. Sophia is never deceived by him. Squire Western has a sure inkling of the unsoundness of his character though he is willing to accept him as his son-in-law on purely prudential considerations. Mrs. Western is not unacquainted with his wickedness for Book XVI, she tells Lady Bellaston, 'I must do Sophy the justice to confess this Blifil is but a hideous kind of fellow...'. Square and Thwackum know him quite well though in their own interest they keep this knowledge unrevealed. In London, Mrs. Miller is never impressed by him. The only person Blifil is able to deceive and impose upon is Squire Allworthy. It may be concluded that though cleverly scheming, Blifil, basically, is not a subtle character like Iago and his initial success is only a reflection on Allworthy's moral blindness.

Unconvincing Portrayal

Like Squire Allworthy, Blifil is a shadowy character, a mere abstraction. His unrelieved wickedness betrays a certain lack of verisimilitude in his portrayal. It is strange how Fielding, a very shrewd and accurate observer and painter of human nature faltered in the case of Blifil and conceived a character who never appears lifelike. Dudden offers an acceptable explanation:

> Fielding's purpose, of course, was to emphasize the contrast between Tom and Blifil, between the good-hearted

scape-grace who, though sound at the core, indulges in shocking escapades, and the false-hearted blackguard whose inner nature is wholly corrupt, though his talk is always pious and his outward deportment exemplary. But he would have achieved his aim more artistically and more convincingly if he had not made Blifil so incredibly wicked.

PARTRIDGE

A Cervantic Figure

Partridge is clearly a Cervantic figure conceived in the mould of Sancho Panza. Only he has been depicted as slightly more intellectual than his French counterpart. His career has a streak of the tragic running through it, but he is himself a comic figure. He is garrulous, pedantic, superstitious, cowardly and gluttonous. When he is first introduced to us, he is an indolent schoolmaster with a shrewish wife. He is convicted of being Tom's father and since he fails to defend himself successfully, he is deprived of his annuity. After the death of his wife, Partridge leaves for ever the parish of Somersetshire and for a long time we hear nothing of him. He reappears in the novel as a barber-surgeon known as Little Benjamin. He sincerely believes Squire Allworthy to be Tom's father and in the hope that just as this child had caused his banishment in the past, it would also work out his restoration to Squire Allworthy's favour in future, he decides to accompany him in his adventures. His role is not very different from that of the Shakespearean clown who, besides producing hilarious comedy, acts as the critic as well. He also contributes a good deal to the development of the action of the novel. In the second volume, he puts, in relief Tom's character and sets off all its variegated colours.

An Incorrigible Babbler

Partridge is an incorrigible and inexhaustible babbler. He talks incessantly but ridiculously. Once he starts talking, he neither stops nor comes to the point. He professes that he can keep secrets most safely, but as a matter of fact, he is willing to blurt out the most personal secrets at the slightest provocation.

Cowardly

Partridge is an arrant coward. The cries of a screech-owl at his window are enough to frighten him out of his bed room. In Book VIII, when Tom is engaged in rescuing the Man of the Hill from some ruffians, Partridge betrays his flagrant timidity and begs Tom not to imperil his life by challenging them. Later, as Tom tries to overpower the highwayman, Partridge is so horrified that he falls flat on the ground in order to hide his face from the encounter. But when the highwayman is completely overpowered, Partridge picks courage to shout, 'kill the villain, sir: run him through the body, kill him this instant'.

Fielding gives a very comic description of the figure Partridge cuts in this situation:

> At this instant, at about a hundred and fifty yards' distance, lay another person on the ground, roaring for mercy in a much louder voice than the highwayman. This was no other than Partridge himself, who endeavouring to make his escape from the" engagement, had been thrown from his horse, and lay flat on his face, not daring to look up, and expecting every minute to be shot.

Superstitions

Partridge is highly superstitious. He fanatically believes in dreams, omens, prophecies, witches, ghosts, hobgoblins, and the devil. His superstitiousness, his timidity, his garrulousness *and* his unexpungable naivete—all combine to make him a very comic figure. His reactions at the staging of *Hamlet* in London expressed so naively produce rich comedy. His interruptions of the tragic narrative of the Man of the Hill take the sting away from his story.

Gluttonous

Partridge loves to lead a comfortable lire. His appetite for beef, bacon and eggs is just insatiable. Being love-sick, Tom hardly drinks or eats; so Partridge feels embarrassed to eat alone. And yet the poor fellow can hardly live without eating. So in a half-comic, half-serious vein, he says to Tom:

> ...what a vast quantity of love must a man have to be able to live upon it without any other food, as you do ? I am positive, I have eaten thirty times as much within these last twenty hours as your honour, and yet I am almost famished.

Dabbling with Latin

In the novel, Partridge appears in various capacities—schoolmaster, clerk, barber, surgeon, tailor. As a schoolmaster, he had picked a little Latin, and is in the habit of punctuating his conversation with Latin words and tags. Though others might be offended with his display of this knowledge, he is himself quite proud of and touchy about it. 'As to the grammar', he boasts, 'I think I may challenge any man living. I think, at least, I have that at my finger's end'.

Motivated by Self-interest

Partridge, invariably in all his actions, is actuated by motives of self-interest but he is intelligent enough to offer very plausible justifications. When Tom expresses his lesire to join army and fight in defence of his King and his country, it is Partridge's cowardice and his sense of self-preservation that tries to keep him back but it is interesting to note how he reasons out his stand:

> ....the soldiers are a wicked kind of people. I never loved to have any thing to do with them. I could hardly bring myself ever to look upon them as Christians. There is nothing but cursing and swearing among them. I wish, your honour would repent before it is too late; and not think of going among them. Evil communication corrupts good manners. That is my principal reason.

Again when Tom becomes penniless, Partridge suggests that he should spend the hundred-pound bill he had found in Sophia's note book. Notice how he argues his point:

> Dishonest ! Heaven forbid I should wrong your honour so much ! But where's the dishonesty in borrowing a little for present spending, since you will be so able to pay the lady hereafter ?

It is his self-interest that induces him to accompany Tom on his hazardous adventures despite his love of comforts and that makes him contemplate joining army despite his cowardice. But it must be said to his credit that he has the saving grace of generosity and his love for Tom is quite genuine. When Tom is utterly penniless, Partridge willingly offers him whatever money he has. Even Tom who frequently loses patience with him finds him an indispensable companion and cannot bear his absence for long. Without Partridge, both Tom's journey to London and his character would have been tedious and colourless.

10

Minor Characters

SQUARE AND THWACKUM

Square and Thwackum are the two private tutors of Tom and Blifil. Square is a philosopher and Thwackum, a divine. Square is rational while Thwackum is orthodox and dogmatic in his views of religion and morality. Both of them are hypocritical and both of them have been berated alike by Fielding. In Book III, chapter 3, Fielding cleverly reveals their true character:

> This gentleman (Square) and Mr. Thwackum scarce ever met without a disputation; for their tenets were indeed diametrically opposite to each other. Square held human nature to be the perfection of all virtue, and that vice was a deviation from our nature, in the same manner as deformity of body is. Thwackum, on the contrary, maintained that the human mind, since the Fall, was nothing but a sink of iniquity, till purified and redeemed by grace. In one point only they agreed, which was, in all their discourses on morality never to mention the word goodness. The favourite phrase of the former was the natural beauty of virtue; that of the latter was the divine power of grace. The former measured all actions by the unalterable rule of right and the eternal fitness of things; the latter decided all matters by authority; but in doing this, he always used the Scriptures and their commentators, as the lawyer doth his Coke upon Lyttleton where the comment is of equal authority with the text.

As stated earlier, both these gentlemen are arrant hypocrites. Thwackum, 'an excellent scholar', 'a most indefatigable teacher', with a great reputation for 'sobriety of manners' and 'devout attachment to religion' is hard-hearted and narrow-minded. He is a stern advocate of the principle of 'doing justice and leaving mercy to Heaven'. But like Blifil, his doctrines are only a ruse to cover up his meanness.

The philosopher Square is equally hypocritical. He is discovered in a very unseemly pose behind the arras in Molly's bed room, and begs of Tom not to be exposed. Yet he takes up a very rigid stand with regard to his judgment on Tom in similar circumstances. However, his death bed repentance partially mitigates the gravity of his sinfulness. For though he does not implicate Blifil, he at least exonerates Tom of much he had been inculpated with and prepares grounds for Tom's reconciliation with Squire Allworthy.

In the persons of Thwackum and Square, Fielding has a fling at the hollowness and futility of religion and philosophy as mere abstractions, without being redeemed by concomitant nobility of motives and intentions. Fielding remarks about them;

> Had not Thwackum too much neglected virtue, and Square, religion, in the composition of their several systems, and had not both utterly discarded all natural goodness of heart, they had never been represented as the objects of derision in this history.

LADY BELLASTON

In Lady Bellaston, Fielding has painted the picture of a dissolute society woman She is a widow, or perhaps a divorcee, no longer young but quite wealthy. Even in the autumn of her life, 'she wore all the gaiety of youth, both in her dress and manner'. But unfortunately for Tom, she is insufferable on account of being cursed with foul breath.

Lady Bellaston is a sex maniac. She uses her wealth to seduce and keep a series of youngmen. It is with her that Sophia takes shelter in London but she uses Sophia almost as a bait to attract Tom and cast on him her own amorous viles for the gratification of her sexual desires. She also exploits Tom's poverty.

Lady Bellaston is an unscrupulous intriguer. When she discovers that Sophia stands in her way with Tom, she feels no compunction at persuading Lord Fellamar to attempt a rape on her, and when she finds that Tom is no longer amenable to her licentious approaches, she plans his ruin and suggests to Lord Fellamar the idea of Tom's impressment. Fortunately she does not succeed in either attempt.

JENNY JONES

Jenny Jones is acknowledged as Tom's mother till the end of the novel when his real parentage is revealed. In return for a handsome amount of money, she takes upon herself the blame for the motherhood of Tom. In the process, she causes irreparable disruption to Partridge's domestic life. Then she disappears from the action of the novel and reappears in Book IX as Mrs. Waters. Her amorous indulgence with Tom at the Upton Inn and her two affairs with Ensign Northerton and Mr. Fitzpatrick reveal her easy-going virtue. However, there is nothing mean or malicious about her character.

Towards the end of the novel, she reveals Tom's parentage, helps in his reconciliation with Squire Allworthy, exposes Blifil and ends up as the wife of Parson Supple.

BRIDGET

Bridget is the sister of Squire Allworthy and the real mother of Tom. Squire Allworthy has a very tender affection for her but that is no index of her merit, for despite her polished exterior, she is low-spirited, mean, selfish and hypocritical. She bribes Jenny to own that she is the mother of the foundling but in the presence of her brother makes a fine show of disgust at her immorality. Her married life with Captain Blifil is marred by frequent clashes of opinion and in the absence of any emotional compatibility between the two, they lead a very wretched life. Yet after the death of Captain Blifil, she looks inconsolable and raises a very touching epitaph to the memory of the deceased.

However, she does make some amends by showing a marked partiality towards Tom in preference to her legitimate son Blifil. Besides, in a letter to her brother from the death bed, she confesses her fault and tries to make up for her earlier moral cowardice.

MRS. WESTERN

Mrs. Western is the comic portrait of a self-opinionated woman. Fielding gives us a fine ironical description of hers in Book VI, chapter 2. She has lived about the Court and is a perfect mistress of 'manners, customs, ceremonies and fashions'. She is well-read in plays, operas, oratorios, poems and romances as well as political pamphlets and journals. She is excellently well-skilled in the doctrine of Amour, but this skill is purely theoretical, for 'her masculine person, which was nearly six-foot high, added to her manners and learning, possibly prevented the other sex from regarding her, notwithstanding her petticoats, in the light of a woman'. Fielding tells us that 'no species of disguise or affectation had escaped her notice; but as to the plain simple workings of honest nature, as she had never seen any such, she could know but little of them'. No wonder that despite her tall claims with regard to her Knowledge, she keeps committing blunders. She believes Blifil to be the object of Sophia's passion and exposes herself to the designs of Mr. Fitzpatrick. If the latter had not chosen a younger woman, she would have been led into a very disastrous marriage.

11

The Structure of *Tom Jones*

Fielding a Superb Craftsman

Fielding is a superb craftsman. He is perhaps the first novelist to conceive of an organic structure for his novels. He neither muddles up an incoherent mass of episodes nor strings them loosely on to the life of his chief protagonist. Instead, he is very careful of those aspects of his art that would ensure the structural unity of the novel. To begin with, he gives his plot an *organic unity.* It means that the majority of incidents contrived by him are held in organic relationship with one another; they grow out of the former incidents and howsoever trifling they might be, they help to advance the story. Next, he observes *a strict harmony between the character, plot and style.* It implies that the incidents are shaped by the characters and the characters are affected by the incidents and the style is adapted to the total design of the novel. Finally, Fielding's moral vision that governs the entire movement of the novel gives it a kind of *moral unity.* Thus the novel is handed down to us as a unified whole. Fielding was the first novelist to give his works this kind of unity. Hence Walter Scott is quite justified in considering him the 'Father of the English novel' and Walter Allen's encomium is well merited: "Fielding was as superb a craftsman in his own way as Henry James."

Narrative Unity

It has now been quite customary to pay homage to Fielding's 'ever-to-be-praised skill as an architect of plot' (the phrase is from Oliver Elton). With some minor qualifications, the plot of *Tom Jones* is still one of the best. Coleridge, indeed, considers it one of the three perfect plots ever planned, the other two being the plots of *Oedipus Tyrannus* and *The Alchemist.* If a digression or two is ignored, this plot is quite in accord with the Aristotelian concept of a fable from which nothing can be taken and to which nothing can be added without damage.

The Unifying Idea

R.S. Crane, in his celebrated article The Plot of *Tom Jones*', illustrates the unity of the plot most convincingly. What is the unifying idea of the novel ? Oliver Elton locates the essence of the story in the sustained concealment and final disclosure of Tom's parentage. Other plausible unifying factors are the love affair of Tom and Sophia, the conflict between Tom and Blifil and the quasi-picaresque sequence of Tom's adventures with women and on the road. All these lines of action are important but none of them subsumes the others to be considered the only principal theme. According to R.S. Crane the unifying idea consists in

> the dynamic systems of actions, extending throughout the novel, by which the divergent intentions and beliefs of a large number of persons of different characters and states of knowledge belonging to or somehow related to the neighbouring families of the Allwonhys and the Westerns are made to co-operate, with the assistance of Fortune, first to bring Tom into an incomplete and precarious union, founded on an affinity of nature in spite of disparity of status, with Allworthy and Sophia; then to separate him as completely as possible from them through actions that impel both of them, one after the other, to reverse their opinions of his character; and then, just as he seems about to fulfil the old prophecy that 'he was certainly born to be hanged', to restore them unexpectedly to him in a more entire and stable union of both affection and fortune than he has known before.

The starting point of everything is Bridget's scheme to provide security for herself and her illegitimate son by palming off Tom on Allworthy as a foundling, with the intention, however, of ultimately informing her brother of the truth. The first part works beautifully; but the second is jeopardised by Bridget's marriage with Captain Blifil. Consequently no early disclosure of Tom's parentage is now possible, and in addition, the boy acquires a potential rival in Blifil. Bridget's scheme involves the departure from the neighbourhood both of Partridge and Jenny Jones and the resolution is postponed for the time being.

Tom Jones has now two problems to face with regard to his relation with Allworthy and Sophia. Tom's feelings for Squire Allworthy are based not on any considerations of self-interest but on the instinctive love of one good nature for another. He has a strong affection for Allworthy, and there can be no change on his part, but Allworthy is capable of giving a contrary verdict on Jones. (His confidence in his own, though erratic, judgment of character, Bridget's favouritism of Tom, aggressive belief in the good intentions of Blifil, confidence in the integrity of the tutors.) Occasions for passing judgment on Tom present themselves increasingly from Tom's fourteenth year. The occasions are given by Tom's well-intentioned but quixotic 'and imprudently managed action towards Black George and his family. Blifil misses no chance of using them to blacken his character in his guardian's eyes. In the first series of these actions, no harm is done to Tom. In Book V, chapter 7, we are told that Allworthy still believes Tom to be one who has 'much goodness, generosity, and honour' in his temper and needs only 'prudence and religion' to make himself actually happy.

The basis of Tom's attachment with Sophia is again the affinity between similar natures. A series of actions bring them together. (Tom's intervention on behalf of Black George, rescue of Sophia, his convalescence at their house, the affair of the muff.) Tom will ever love Sophia. Sophia also is a better judge of human nature than Squire Allworthy. She is not unacquainted with the Tom-Molly affair, still she loves Tom. Squire Western, however, does not approve of their marriage-Tom's parentage is dubious and this marriage holds no material prospects. Neither Sophia nor Tom has any intentions of violating filial piety or betraying ingratitude. So unless some event happens to change Tom's position as a foundling, there can be no resolution.

Such an event could happen, for Bridget has confided her secret in Dowling, but fortune intervenes in favour of Blifil. A complex action now begins with Allworthy's illness and ends with Tom's expulsion and Sophia's flight. The separating action of the novel comes to its first major climax with Tom resolved, for the sake of Sophia, to renounce her and leave the country, and with Sophia, unable to endure the prospect of a marriage with Blifil, determined to seek refuge in London with her cousin Lady Bellaston.

The secret of Tom's parentage is known partly or wholly to at least three persons-Partridge, Jenny Jones and Dowling, Tom, now on the road, is more likely to meet them now than before. In fact, he does meet them one after the other. His meeting with Partridge reveals that he is not Partridge's son. From his meeting with others, no immediate resolution follows. In the case of Jenny Jones, it so happens that she does not meet Partridge at the Upton Inn and although Dowling is prepared to sell the secret, Tom's own disinterestedness postpones the probability of an early revelation.

The events at the Upton Inn, in the meanwhile, complicate the situation. Tom has first an angry encounter with Fitzpatrick (because of his gallantry to Jenney) and then misses Sophia, who departs at once on learning of his infidelity and makes her way to London. Sophia is disturbed not so much by his misconduct with Jenny as by Partridge's free use of her name in public.

Tom finds his way to Sophia in London, but he is seduced into the affair with Lady Bellaston. He also incurs the wrath of Lady Bellaston and thus begin a fresh series of efforts to separate Tom and Sophia. The first of these, the attempted rape of Sophia is thwarted by her timely rescure by Western. Imminent marriage of Sophia with Blifil is, however, threatened. Lady Bellaston acts two ways. She sends to Sophia the letter she had received from Tom and she arranges for Tom's kidnapping by a press-gang. She succeeds with Sophia but not with Tom.

Things gradually improve for Tom. Mrs. Miller intercedes with Squire Allworthy and Sophia on behalf of Tom. The characters in the know of the secret assemble, in the meanwhile, in close proximity of Allworthy. A reversal of Tom's position needs first a reversal of Allworthy's impression of Tom. This is prepared by Mrs. Miller's insistence upon his present goodness, but the decisive event is the letter from the dying and repentant Square. Tom is absolved from much though Blifil is not implicated. The intervention of fortune, aided by Blifil's rashness, brings about the revelation so long delayed. Fitzpatrick's wound does not prove as serious as it appeared; Jenny goes to Allworthy with her story; finally Dowling is questioned, the revelation is complete, and Bridget's intended disclosure of her secret is at last made.

The union with Sophia is likewise prepared by Mrs. Miller, who is able to convince her that Tom's letter proposing marriage to Lady Bellaston was at worst an indiscretion. Allworthy intervenes on Tom's behalf. Western advocates for him as he did earlier for Blifil, but the resolution comes only with Sophia's meeting with the repentant youngman.

The Symmetry of the Plot

This, then, in essence, is the plot of *Tom Jones* and Fielding has conducted it with consummate symmetry. The whole novel consists of eighteen Books, further divided into extremely well-defined three parts. First six Books deal with Tom's life in the countryside; in the next six Books when; Tom is practically on the road, the novel follows the picaresque tradition, and the last six Books deal with the life in London. Exactly at the centre-Books IX and X-is placed the comic peripety, the hilarious comedy at the Upton Inn. These two Books cover only twelve hours. This is perhaps the shortest duration of time covered in any single unit of the novel. Hence it could be said that the dramatic character of the novel is best sustained at the centre. The centre remtroduces Jenny Jones into the novel. Now Jenny is the person who by taking upon herself Bridget's guilt, helps' in the concealment of Tom's true parentage, but it is she who, at the end of the novel, by exposing Blifil, brings about the revelation and the final resolution. Again, when Sophia arrives at Upton, she is pursuing Tom, but having learnt of Tom's escapade with Mrs. Waters, she departs in indignation and now it is Tom who has to pursue her. Thus the centre brings a complete reversal in their love. The two major digressions in the novel, the story of the Man of the Hill and Mrs. Fitzpatrick's account, are symmetrically interpolated about the centre-Books VIII and XL. Then there are contrasts and similarities to add to the structural unity of the novel. Tom's rural entanglement with Molly is balanced by his urban involvement with Lady Bellaston. Sophia's first interview with Blifil is paralleled by her misadventure with Lord Fellamar. The curtain scene in Molly's bed room has a parallel in the curtain scenes in Tom's bed room at Mrs. Miller's lodgings.

Structural Unity through Repeated Appearance of the Same Object or the Same Person

The structural unity of the novel is preserved through repeated appearance of either the same object or the same person. Sophia's hundred-pound bill as well as her muff makes repeated appearances in the novel. The hundred-pound bill puts Tom on Sophia's track; later it provides Tom with an excuse to meet Sophia at Lady Bellaston's. The muff when retrieved from fire by Sophia early in the novel assures Tom that Sophia loves him. At the Upton

Inn, Sophia leaves it in Tom's bed to make Tom regret his indiscretion and to make him pursue Sophia. Dowling and Jenny Jones cross Tom's path quite frequently. Ensign Northerton is the person with whom Tom Jones quarrels when he picks an acquaintance with some military personnel but it is also from him that he rescues Jenny Jones. The highwayman makes an effort to deprive Tom of his money, but it is later discovered that he is related to Mrs. Miller.

Parallel or Contrasted Characters

The structural unity is also achieved through parallel or contrasted characters. In the early part of the book, Squire Allworthy's wisdom and his moral restraint are contrasted with Squire Western's stupidity and his rash impetuosity. Then Tom's good nature is contrasted with Blifil's malice. Sophia's innocence in her love is in contrast with Molly's guilt. Sophia is also to be contrasted with Lady Bellaston and Mrs. Fitzpatrick and a comparison between Tom Jones and Nightingale is also not out of place.

Blemishes

Coming to the blemishes, there are two major and three minor digressions in this narrative. The two major digressions are the story of the Man of the Hill and Mrs. Fitzpatrick's account in Books VIII and XI. The three minor digressions are Tom's presence at the puppet show, and his encounter with the gypsies and later his presence at Garrick's performance of *Hamlet in* London. While on purely artistic grounds, these digressions cannot be defended, at least an explanation can be ventured. The Man of the Hill offers a contrast to Tom and helps to underline the sanity of Tom's attitude to life. Tom has not been less wronged than the Man of the Hill. But Tom does not withdraw from the society. Had Tom also grown as indifferent and apathetic to humanity, he would not have imperiled his life to rescue the old man. Mrs. Fitzpatrick's account is even less objectionable, for it serves to warn Sophia of the dangers of displaced attachment and clandestine marriage. Besides, for these two digressions, Fielding enjoys, at least, the sanction of the epic tradition. Of the minor digressions. Tom's encounter with the gypsies is neither very interesting nor of much service to the plan of the novel, though the gypsy law has some moral implications in the context of the novel. Partridge's comments on Garrick's performance of *Hamlet* arouse much fun.

A few more lapses in the story could also be pointed out. Some of the coincidences are a bit too improbable. It would be difficult to accept as probable the sequence of arrivals and departures that Fielding contrives at the Upton Inn. Tom, on the track of Sophia, first comes across the beggar who has picked up her pocket-book, then meets the merry gentleman who has seen her passing by, and finally, in the alehouse, encounters the very guide who has conducted her to Mariden. In London, Squire Western appears at the right moment to rescue Sophia from being raped by Lord Fellamar. Such a series of lucky occurrences, though not impossible, are in deed too opportune to strike as credible.

Finally the ending of the story is a bit hurried and huddled. In the last Books, a number of momentous actions are massed together confusedly. Fielding himself appears to have been conscious that the narrative is unduly compressed in Book XVIII, for he writes:

> When thou (the reader "I has pursued the many great events which this Book will produce, thou wilt think the number of pages contained in it scarce sufficient to tell the story.

Harmony of Plot and Character

In a good novel, a strict correspondence between *plot* and *character* is very essential. In fact, Henry James declares that character *is* action. In *Tom Jones,* action follows logically from the characters. Tom's dismissal by Allworthy is the climactic action of the first third of the novel. This is precipitated by Squire Allworthy's misplaced confidence in his capability to judge coupled with Tom's joyous drunkenness and his indiscretion with Molly. At the centre of the novel, Tom's involvement with Mrs. Waters creates a whole series of new complications in his relationship with Sophia; so does Tom's behaviour with Lady Bellaston at the end of the novel. Squire Western's faith in established social values and his hot-headed affection for his daughter also play a very important role. Blifil's execrable self-interestedness and jealousy first act to degrade Tom in the eyes of others but later they help in the final resolution.

Fielding's Moral Vision Governs the Entire Movement

The whole design of *Tom Jones* is governed by Fielding's moral vision. In *Tom Jones,* his subject is human nature and his purpose is threefold: to exhibit the loveliness of virtue and the ugliness of vice; to convince men that their interest lies in the pursuit of virtue and the avoidance of vice; and finally, to inculcate the lesson that virtue needs to be guided by discretion. As the action in *Tom Jones* is unfolded, this purpose is aptly realised.

The Style of the Novel is Suited to Its Subject

Fielding's style—light, gay, mildly ironical-is quite suited to his purpose. It makes one conscious of one's follies without causing undue bitterness. It points out but does not condemn, hence it provokes reflection.

Conclusion

To conclude, it would not be an exaggeration to say that the world had not seen a greater epic than *Tom Jones* since the days of Homer. The characters and action are wonderfully diversified, yet all is so natural, and so pleasant. While reading *Tom Jones,* one is pleasantly struck with certain harmony of composition. Thackeray was quite justified to pronounce that as a work of construction, *Tom Jones* is 'quite a wonder'.

12

Tom Jones As a Comic Epic in Prose

Fielding himself described *Tom Jones* as a comic epic in prose. That he had hit upon a new genre of literature and was keen to explore its possibilities is clear from his conscious attempts to expound a theory about it. He had behind him a tradition, though not fully established or developed, which he could adopt to suit his personal needs. Homer had long ago produced a comic epic which according to Aristotle bore the same relation to comedy as *The Iliad* and *The Odyssey* did to tragedy. The concept of a prose epic was also familiar. A work might, with appropriateness, be styled as a prose epic if it had all the parts of an epic poem—fable, action, character, sentiment, diction—with the single exception of metre. Combining these ideas of the comic epic and the prose epic, Fielding evolved a new genre—comic epic in prose.

A Comic Epic in Prose, Comic Romance, Burlesque, Serious Romance, History

In his Preface to *Joseph Andrews,* Fielding has differentiated his comic epic in prose from both a comic romance and a serious romance:

> Now, a comic romance is a comic epic poem in prose; differing from comedy, as the serious epic from tragedy: its action being more: extended and comprehensive; containing a much larger circle of incidents, and introducing a greater variety of characters. It differs from the serious romance in its fable and action, in this; that as in the one these are grave and solemn, so in the other they are light and ridiculous: it differs in its characters by introducing persons of inferior rank, and consequently of inferior manners, whereas the grave romance sets the highest before us: lastly, in its sentiments and diction; by preserving the ludicrous instead of the sublime.

Fielding also tells us that like an epic, his comic epic in prose embraces dignity and solemnity of purpose.

The comic epic may also be differentiated from the burlesque:

> Burlesque is ever the exhibition of what is monstrous and where our delight if we examine it, arises from the surprising absurdity whereas the comic is strictly confined to the just imitation of nature which to an accurate observer is sufficiently ridiculous. In the comic epic, while the

> characters and sentiments must always be perfectly natural, a certain burlesque drollery in style is permissible in the narrative or descriptive parts.

The comic epic is also different from the purely fanciful French heroic romance. These romances described persons who never existed nor could exist, events that never happened nor could happen. The world of these romances had no spiritual affinity with the actual world. In his comic epic, however, Fielding claims that 'everything is copied from the book of nature and scarce a character or action produced which I have not taken from my own experiences'. Perhaps that is why he prefers to call his novel a history. But *history* does not describe *Tom Jones* accurately. One will have to use the word *epic*:

> The epic writer reveals, as the ordinary historian does not, the basic truths of human nature no matter when or where or under what conditions it exists, had existed or will exist. History describes temporal and local phases of human life while an epic reveals universal truths.

What, then, is a Comic Epic in Prose ?

Thus a comic epic in prose chiefly promises a variety of characters involved in a very comprehensive action. The novelist's tone is light, even frivolous, and he gives mildly satirical, ironical exposition of the ridiculous. It is epical in scale, and it is comic since it concerns the ridiculous in human life. It is not romance since it is highly, down-to-earth realistic. It is not history for it is not a superficial study of events, nor is it a burlesque, for a burlesque distorts while it does not. Behind the frivolous tone of the novelist, there is a strict moral responsibility which he shares with the writers of the serious epics. What Fielding was attempting was an entirely new species of literature in his language and he was right to claim, "This kind of writing I do not remember to have seen hitherto attempted in our language."

The comic tone in 'Tom Jones'

The comic tone of the novel is established from the very beginning when Mrs. Wilkins, unexpectedly summoned by her master, confronts him in what she thinks to be a grossly indecent dress for a gentleman—an ironic comment on the prudence of decency in dress—and gives a loud shriek. Squire Allworthy's confidence in the Tightness of his judgment, his insistence on meeting out justice and his expulsion both of Tom Jones and Partridge ironically revealing an utter lack of insight into human nature are treated quite lightly.

In Book II, we have a highly comic description of the battle between Partridge and his wife which is sparked off by Mrs. "Partridge's suspicion that her husband is the foundling's father. She attacks the poor schoolmaster with 'tongue, teeth and hands' reducing him to a bloody wreck, but feeling tired of this exercise falls into a fit of weeping and succeeds in winning the sympathy of the neighbours. The same Book gives a graphic description of Captain Blifil's ecstatic pleasures that he experiences by contemplating an early death of Squire Allworthy. It is amusing to note that it is the Captain himself who dies and not the Squire. The description of the bitter, rift-ridden wedded life of the Blifils ends with a description of the warm and moving tribute engraved on the Captain's tombstone by 'his inconsolable wife'. This is a very quiet but very effective comic touch. In his Preface to *Joseph Andrews,* Fielding says that the only source of the true ridiculous is affectation and affectation proceeds from either vanity or hypocrisy. Captain Blifil's conjured-up pleasures betray this vanity while the epitaph is sheer hypocrisy and Fielding uses both of them to produce good comedy.

In Book V, Tom's bacchic celebration of his patron's recovery and his indiscreet sexual revelry with Molly that results in a quarrel with Blifil, Squire and Thwackum produces interesting comedy. The unexpected arrival of Squire Western and the miscalculated cause of Sophia's fainting in the light of the amorous encounter that had already taken place between Tom and Sophia appears quite amusing.

Book VI opens with violent outbursts of Squire Western as he gets the news of Sophia's being in love:

> How ! in love ! in love without acquainting me ! I'll disinherit her; I'll turn her out of doors stark naked without a farthing.

This violent display of temper is as ridiculous as his later approbatory outburst when Sophia's aunt interrupts him to remark that she might have fallen in love with a youth of his choice. Squire Western immediately says, "If she marries the man I would ha' her, she may love whom she pleases. I sha'n't trouble my head about that."

The meeting between Blifil and Sophia in the same Book is also dealt with in a comic spirit. Nobody speaks for the first quarter of an hour: then Blifil suddenly breaks forth into a torrent of far-fetched verbosity answered by Sophia in monosyllables. This meeting has a parallel later in the encounter between Sophia and Lord Fellamar which produces comedy in a mock-tragic frame. The stereotyped extravagance of Lord Fellamar's declaration and the fortuitous rescue of Sophia cannot be mistaken for tragedy.

The scene at the Upton Inn occupies a central position in the structure of *Tom Jones.* It also produces the height of comedy. Tom and his companion, the dishavelled Mrs. Waters, enter the Upton Inn and the landlady, apprehending a gross violation of the sanctity of the premises, abruptly pounces upon them. The ensuing battle involves soldiers of both the sexes; the weapons include the tongue, the broomstick, the cudgel and the fist. This fight over, another, of amorous nature, follows. As Tom gets busy with the beef and the ale, his fair companion starts playing her 'artillery' to subdue him. Fielding employs mock-heroic style and diction to describe this battle of wits. He even invokes the graces before he begins this description. Finally Mrs. Waters wins and enjoys the fruit of her victory. This is followed by Mr. Fitzpatrick's misunderstanding that Mrs. Waters is his own wife, his quarrel with Tom, and Mrs. Waters's cries of rape to save herself from being termed a whore. When Sophia arrives with Mrs. Honour, the latter indulges in very comic antics in the kitchen in an effort to assume gentility which she clearly lacks. Even more boisterous comedy is produced with the arrival of Squire Western hot on the trail of Sophia. There is a fine parody of the state of law and justice in contemporary England when Tom is first charged with the theft of Sophia's muff and then acquitted on Susan's evidence. Mr. Fitzpatrick's efforts to claim kindred with Squire Western and his negligence of all pleas are also comic in tone.

Whenever the situation is in danger of getting a tragic coloring and whenever the chief protagonists find themselves in some precarious predicament, Fielding provides a comic turn or offers a timely resolution. Torn between his love for Sophia and moral responsibility for Molly, Tom finds himself in a state of acute mental conflict. This conflict is resolved by the discovery of the philosopher Square behind the curtain in Molly's bed room. The whole scene ends practically in a farce. This pattern is repeated in London when Lady Bellaston is behind the curtain and Honour indulges in scurrilous denouncement and later when Honour is behind the curtain and Tom Jones's meeting with Lady Bellaston is interrupted by the appearance of Nightingale in a drunken state. The acrimonious exchange between the two ladies and their subsequent reconciliation offers hilarious comedy.

The autobiographical account of the Man of the Hill and Mrs. Fitzpatrick's story are tragic but the comic tone of the author saves them from being unrelieved tragedy. In the case of the Man of the Hill, it is Partridge's attitude and his amusing interruptions of the narrative that extenuate its tragic effect, while Mrs. Fitzpatrick's account being a parody of sentimental romance contains within itself many comic possibilities.

Fielding's handling of his characters also has a touch of the comic. The excessive solemnity of Squire Allworthy and its ironic implications have already been commented upon. Squire Western is portrayed purely in the comic vein. His violence is more amusing than horrifying. It is really interesting to know how he abandons the furious pursuit of his daughter and joins a party of fox hunters since it is such a fine day for hunting. The moral scruples of Tom and the justification he gives for his involvement with Lady Bellaston have a comic touch. "Gallantry to the ladies was among his principles of honour," says Fielding, "and he held it as much incumbent on him to accept a challenge to love as if it had been a challenge to fight." Even the hypocrisy and villainy of Square, Thwackum and Blifil are unfolded through comedy rather than through satire. Fielding, by nature, was too genial to attempt a satire or a lampoon.

'Tom Jones' is Epical in Scale

If *Tom Jones* is comic in spirit, it is epical in scale. It offers at least forty well-portrayed characters drawn from different cross-sections of society. There are lords, justices of peace, lawyers, servants, highwaymen, parsons, innkeepers, soldiers, gypsies, country squires and many others.

Epic Unities

In *Tom Jones,* Fielding also shows his concern for the epic unities. The headings of the various Books indicate the time taken by the action described in them. Book I tells us 'as much of the birth of the foundling as is necessary'. Books II and III summarise events till Tom is arrived at the age of seventeen. Book IV is described as 'containing a year'; Book V 'containing the portion of time somewhat longer than half a year'; Book VI three weeks. Once the antecedent material is given in the first four Books, the action is made to come well within a year. The action in all the important epics, *The Iliad, The Odyssey, The Aenied,* is completed within a year.

The action is comprehensive and well extended in space. It includes within its folds the countryside, the highways and the great urban society of London. The rural as well as the urban society is portrayed almost in entirety. The action is so distributed that three units consisting of six Books each strictly observe the unity of place.

But the action of the novel is given an organic unity which is far more important than mere bringing the major action within a certain time limit or observing the unity of place in three different sections of the novel. *Tom Jones* is not a chronicle and its action is constructed according to dramatic principles. Everything turns about a single action—the discovery of a child in Squire Allworthy's bed and the resolution of the mystery of its parentage. But for two digressions—the story of the Man of the Hill and Mrs. Fitzpatrick's account—the novel has a single, whole, organically perfect action. And even the two digressions have a certain thematic relevance and are strictly in accordance with the epic tradition.

Mock-heroic Style

Fielding has freely used mock-heroic style and diction. In Book IV, the jealous attack made upon Molly by some women who resent her fine dress has a clear touch of the mock-heroic. Even the title given to the chapter describing this battle suggests its mock-heroic character: A Battle Sung by the Muse in the Homeric Style and which none but the Classical Reader can Taste. The entire Upton episode has been written in the mock-heroic style. Even the rape attempted on Sophia is described in the same style. Notice, for example, the description of Sophia's tears: it is not a tear which trickles down her lovely cheek; rather 'a shower of tears ran down into her bosom'. Apart from this we can notice some other details of the epic formula also. There is a generous sprinkling of Homeric similes and while describing Sophia, there is even a serious invocation to the Muse.

Solemnity of Purpose

Fielding called his novel an epic also on account of the very high notions he had of the purpose of the novel. He never thought that a novel was merely a source of entertainment. He considered it a very serious form of literature imbued with as serious a moral purpose as an epic. He felt that a novel could be a fit vehicle for profoundly influencing human thought and behaviour and used it so. In *Tom Jones,* his purpose was to show the loveliness of virtue and the ugliness of vice, to suggest that one's interest lay in the pursuit of virtue and the avoidance of vice and to emphasise the need of directing one's good intentions intelligently—a very solemn purpose indeed.

The Prose in 'Tom Jones'

'In prose' is not merely a tag to fill out the phrase 'comic epic in prose'. It was a well-known belief that poetry is appropriate to the expression of the more elevated thoughts and the celebration of great actions. 'In prose' plants us firmly once and for all in the ordinary world with which Fielding was primarily pre-occupied. As a realist attempting a comic epic he found prose with a comic turn given to its phrase as a very suitable medium although when he goes really high in *Tom Jones,* his prose turns lyrical and soars high like 'an archangel brooding over mankind'.

Conclusion

If we refer to Aristotle's original triangulation, we find that non-dramatic equivalent of the comedy is lampoon, of tragedy, epic. With the new opening before him, Fielding takes cross bearings on the old land marks and attempts a comic epic. 'In prose' gives him a third bearing and his triangulation is complete. He leaves an old track, but he does not get lost. W.L. Renwick in *Essays and Studies,* rightly remarks:

> In that great phrase 'comic epic in prose', Fielding evoked a critical tradition, claimed his authority, asserted right of the new.......to the craft of the comedy and the dignity of the epic and assumed moral responsibilities of both along with the freedom of prose.

13

Fielding's Concept of Morality in *Tom Jones*

Fielding's concept of morality as depicted in *Tom Jones* has occasioned startingly contrasted comments. Richardson denounced the novel as 'a dissolute book...a profligate performance'. Dr. Johnson was even more severe and uncharitable; he strongly rebuked Hannah More for alluding to a passage in *Tom Jones.* In her *Memoirs,* she reproduces a remark once Dr. Johnson made to her in this context:

> I am shocked to hear you quote from so vicious a book. I am sorry to hear you have read it: a confession which no modest lady should ever make. 1 scarcely know a more corrupt book.

John Hawkins attacks the book as 'seemingly intended to sap the foundation of that morality which it is the duty of parents and all public instructors to inculcate in the minds of young people'. Even Carlyle was contemptuous of it on account of the alleged moose morality' of its hero.

On the contrary, Sir Walter Scott was convinced that Fielding's great novel would do no one any harm. Coleridge strongly insisted on the essential healthiness of Fielding's work in contrast with the essential unhealthiness of Richardson's. According to Coleridge, coming to Fielding after having read Richardson's *Clarissa* is like emerging from 'a sick room heated by stoves' into 'an open lawn on a breezy day in May'. Lytton proclaimed Fielding a 'deep, accurate and scientific moralist'. Twentieth century criticism also, generally, is appreciative of Fielding's moral point of view.

It would be highly unfair to dub Fielding as immoral. It is true that in *Joseph Andrews* he is not seriously concerned with any moral purpose: he sets up as a moral theorist only later than *Joseph Andrews.* In *The History of Jonathan Wild the Great,* he presents an antithesis between greatness and goodness. *Amelia* in which the author deliberately lays himself out to expose the civil practices of his times is loaded with didactic matter. Fielding wanted to awaken the public conscience against the corruption among the officials and the abuses of the prison houses and the law courts in order to bring about at least partial reformation.

Three-fold Purpose in 'Tom Jones'

Tom Jones is not devoid of this instructive tendency. In his dedication to *Tom Jones,* Fielding makes it eminently clear that he wrote the novel not merely to picture but also to edify. He declares his intention as being threefold: to exhibit the loveliness of virtue, to convince men that their interest lies in the pursuit of virtue and the avoidance of vice, and to inculcate the lesson that virtue needs to be guided by discretion.

The loveliness of virtue is manifest in Fielding's noble characters like Squire Allworthy and Sophia. These characters are not perfect. Squire Allworthy is erratic in, though stubbornly confident of his judgment. At times, Sophia too can be obstinate-like. But these flaws make these characters appear only more human and enhance their appeal and effectiveness. Fielding knows that figures of abnormal excellence and virtue appear too wooden. The beauty of virtue is displayed in these characters with such appropriateness that they engage the admiration of all unprejudiced minds. Along with the beauty of virtue has been portrayed the ugliness of vice. Blifil and Lady Bellaston have been depicted as heinous characters and they provoke disgust.

Next, Fielding insists that one's true interest lies in the pursuit of virtue and the avoidance of vice. In this insistence, Fielding dissociates himself from the prudential moralists like Richardson, who regards virtue as a great source of material comfort and prosperity. As a matter of fact, virtue and material prosperity rarely appear together. Fielding was aware that a virtuous man, by reason of this innocence, makes himself an easy victim to deceit and treachery and hence is afflicted with untoward suffering. Yet, he believed that even amidst this suffering, a virtuous man enjoys a 'solid inward comfort of mind'. To expect any material benefit from being virtuous is to desecrate virtue. The highest form of happiness consists in 'inward comfort of mind', and this 'inward comfort of mind' is obtainable only by virtue That is why Fielding makes Squire Allworthy say, "Believe me, there is more pleasure, even in this world, in an innocent and virtuous life than in one debauched and vicious."

Vice is ugly, though its ugliness may lie concealed for a while. And vice can never bring true, abiding happiness. The vicious man should always be suffering from horror and anxiety, internal disquiet and uneasiness. Besides, vice always comes to an unhappy end. It is in the nature of vice to bring upon those who practise it sufficient punishment though this punishment might be delayed. "Good heavens !" exclaims Squire Allworthy, "in what miserable distresses do vice and imprudence involve men ! How much beyond our designs are the effects of wickedness sometimes carried."

Finally, it is man's duty to exercise prudence and to guard his virtue against all externals. "Prudence and circumspection are necessary even to the best of men," says Squire Allworthy. "They are a guard to virtue without which it can never be safe." That is what Jom Jones finally comes to realise. His bacchic celebration of his benefactor's recovery can be explained but not excused. Temptations are not wanting in this world. How easy it is for Black George to fall a prey to the temptation of having easy five hundred pounds or for Tom Jones to succumb to the enticing viles of Molly Seagrim. And, to be sure, there is no dearth of women like Molly Seagrim, Mrs. Waters, Mrs. Fitzpatrick and Lady Bellaston. So one has to be assiduously vigilant against all temptations. It is quite in the fitness of things that Tom Jones wins Sophia's hand only when he has controlled his temptations.

Fielding's Concept of Virtue and Vice: Virtue is Goodness of Heart; Vice is Hypocrisy

Perhaps the concepts of both virtue and vice need further elucidation. Virtue, according to Fielding, is a matter of one's inner being. It is not external respectability; it is goodness of heart. In making an estimate of one's personality, one's motives and intentions, even one's vague, half-realised instincts have to be given as much importance as one's externalised, tangible actions. Apparently, Blifil is almost irreproachable in his virtue and respectability. He is saintly in his talk, prudent in his actions and most discreet in his behaviour. But inwardly he is totally selfish and malignant. Hidden under the veneer of his piety and respectability is one of the meanest, most scheming, most treacherous personalities one can come across in the entire range of English fiction.

Tom's goodness of heart is revealed time and again in his generosity towards others. Even in the face of severe punishment, he maintains that he was all alone while poaching in Squire Western's orchard, for he knows that if Black George's involvement is even hinted at, it might cost him his job. He sells the horse, his dearest possession at the moment, in order to provide financial relief to the family of the gamekeeper. On way to London, he is challenged by the highwayman, and he overpowers him; but when he comes to know the real motive of his desperate attempt, he willingly parts with half of his possessions to help the highwayman's starving family. Later he is ready to part with the money he has received from Lady Bellaston to help the same highwayman. He also makes efforts to secure marriage for his landlady's daughter pregnant by his fellow lodger Nightingale. Tom Jones can never bear to see anyone in distress; and immediately proceeds to help him at whatever personal cost it might be. That is virtue.

But even the most virtuous-looking actions of Blifil are motivated by the basest intentions He sets the bird free not because confinement is a sin but because release of this bird would cause acute mental torture to Sophia as well as to Tom. He exposes Tom Jones to Squire Allworthy not to give an evidence of his truthfulness but to degrade him in the latter's eyes. He wants to marry Sophia out of pure malice and avariciousness. This marriage would entitle him to Squire Western's riches. But more than that it would be a sign of certain victory over his rival Tom. Blifil is an unredeemed hypocrite and in Fielding's code of moral values, hypocrisy is the greatest vice. Hypocrisy should be difficult to detect, since its exterior is so attractive. Nevertheless, Fielding hints at a key symptom. Hypocrisy involves an unusual degree of self-control, so a hypocrite normally lacks strong passions. Fielding alerts us to be on our guard while dealing with a person of extreme politeness, extreme piety and unusual self-control. Such a person might be a Blifil or a Thwackum.

The Importance of Feeling

In the moral teaching of Fielding, feeling holds the first place. The man who feels very keenly is capable of great happiness whether real or imaginary. He feels the joys of others as deeply as his own. The goodness of heart is essential for a man of feeling; in fact, it is an inevitable human condition for him. This doctrine William Empson puts very clearly and cogently:

> If good by nature, you can imagine other people's feelings so directly that you can have an impulse to act on them as if they were your own and this is the source of your greatest pleasures as well as of your only genuinely unselfish actions.

The fact that Fielding gives his hero both feeling and goodness of heart quite clearly proves that Fielding never lost sight of the moral perspective while he was writing *Tom Jones.*

Tom's Sexual Involvements and Fielding's Moral Scheme

There are many moral lapses or offences in *Tom Jones* which have been given a much more tolerant treatment than any puritan moralist would have accorded them. Defoe and Richardson, for example, are unsparing in their denunciation of drunkenness, but Tom's drinking spree gets no reprobation from Fielding. But it is ultimately the sexual issue which is most crucial to Fielding's moral scheme. Most of Fielding's puritannic contemporaries felt offended with the apparent indulgence with which he treated his hero's sexual digressions. This definitely calls for a closer scrutiny of Tom's sexual involvements. To begin with, we notice that Fielding has placed Tom in certain extenuating circumstances. Tom is the seduced rather than the seducer. It is Molly Seagrim, the senior and more experienced partner who leads him into the affair. At the Upton Inn also, Tom appears to be a helpless victim in the hands of Mrs. Waters's artful coquetry since she makes use of her full artillery to him. In the case of Lady Bellaston, it is a sense of gratitude for the financial assistance he receives from her and his awareness that only Lady Bellaston can bring him to his beloved Sophia that do not let him snap this bond of shame. None of these affairs are of Tom's own creating, but once he gets into them, it must be said to his credit that he conducts himself very honourably. Even when he is so deeply in love with Sophia, he never thinks of forsaking Molly. The timing of these affairs also deserves attention. Tom's relationship with Molly precedes his love for Sophia. His affair with Mrs. Waters occurs at a time when he has no hope whatsoever of ever meeting Sophia again. And he falls to Lady Bellaston's viles because he thinks that she can get him in touch with Sophia. As the plot develops, he gradually learns to control himself. He strongly and successfully resists the amorous advances of Mrs. Fitzpatrick and turns down a very attractive marriage offer from Arabella Hunt. It is only then that Sophia relents to accept him as her husband. Thus it would be wrong to say that Fielding endorses or even condones his hero's incontinence. He simply places sexual virtue and sexual vice in a broad moral perspective and takes a lenient, rather a human, view of Tom's sexual aberrations. Fielding believes that virtue does not consist in rigid suppression of instinct. A certain carefree animality—the like of which we find in Tom—is a sign of mental health. It is decidedly better than Clarissa's frigid virtue. It only needs circumspection so that it is not misled.

William Empson suggests that there is a moral point in leaving Tom Jones a bastard:

> He is to inherit Paradise Hall because he is held to deserve it, not because the plot has been dragged round to make him the legal heir.

To conclude, Fielding attempts to broaden our moral sense rather than intensify its punitive operations against licentiousness. His attitude to sexual ethics is essentially normative; it certainly does not, as Boswell said, 'encourage a strained and rarely possible virtue', but rather reflects, as Leslie Stephen puts it, 'the code by which men of sense generally govern their conduct'. In brief, his concept of morality is based upon an intimate study of human nature and it is most healthy and liberal.

14

Additional Themes in *Tom Jones*

The Hunt

Fielding has skilfully used the sport of 'hunting' as a metaphor to describe relationships in the novel. The pursuit of characters driven by passion has been compared to a hunter's pursuit of his prey. The image of hunting is effectively created throughout the novel. In the first half of the novel, Sophia pursues Tom, metaphorically and literally but the roles are reversed in the second half which narrates the pursuit of Tom for Sophia. The parallel can be drawn between the sport of hunting where the 'hunter' can at times become the 'hunted', as in the case of Tom and Sophia.

Fielding elaborates this theme into a complex pattern of pursuits and flights. As an actual hunter may sometimes find his prey captured by another, similarly, when Squire Western finds Sophia, she is being abducted by Lord Fellamar, another 'hunter' looking for an easy prey. Fielding elaborates this theme more subtly. Squire Western, Sophia's father, is a bundle of unbridled instincts who spends more time hunting than doing anything else. He shares the vitality and lack of restraint of Tom. He loves his daughter a lot and showers high praise on her when he comes to prefer her to his hunting dogs. When Sophia goes hunting with him, Fielding shows her affection for her father. She then falls from her horse into the arms of Tom Jones. In this way, Fielding gives us a metaphor for her passion for Tom, which pulls her away from her father. Squire Western, discovering his daughter to be missing immediately sets out to hunt her down as well.

The Theatre

The narrator in *Tom Jones* writes that the world is a stage, borrowing a theme used by Shakespeare. The various characters in the play are presented playing false roles and assuming an appearance which is far removed from reality. Molly and Blifil wear masks of innocence as Lady Bellaston wears the mask of chastity. Tom meets Lady Bellaston at a masquerade, where she greets masked friends as though they were in her drawing room having tea. But when she finds Tom and Sophia in her own drawing room, she and Tom act like strangers to each other. The theme of theatre predominates in the second half of the novel, when the characters reach Upton Inn from where the story assumes the cruder, more frenzied quality of a farce. In *Joseph Andrews*, Fielding presents Lady Booby who "prepares a face to meet the faces" that she meets.

Marriage for Love Vs Marriage for Money

With this theme Fielding gets a chance to explore the extent of children's duty to fulfill their parents' desires and the need to seek their own love. Also, he brings forth clearly the English class prejudice. Squire Western is against the match of Tom and Sophia because Tom is poor and more importantly he has no lineage. He thwarts his daughter's desires and imprisons her till she agrees to marry Master Blifil, who belongs to aristocracy. His greed demands that his daughter marry Blifil for his money, knowing well that she is in love with Tom. Sophia is faced with a difficult choice and is torn between her love for her father and her own desire to marry Tom, wherein lies her happiness. Fielding attacks the cold and callous attitude of Mr. and Mrs. Western who believe marriage to be an alliance between estates, rather than an expression of love and care between husband and wife. Fielding cites other examples of this conflict—for example, the Quaker who is angry because he believes his daughter has made a foolish match by marrying for love rather than money. Yet, towards the end of *Tom Jones* Fielding discloses Tom to have aristocratic lineage before he can marry Sophia. It leaves one thinking whether Fielding himself has aristocratic prejudices, after all !

Wisdom

Plato's philosophy regarded wisdom as the highest ideal a man could achieve. This ideal is sought by the hero, Tom who lacks it completely at the beginning of the novel. His journey is a quest for 'Sophia' which in Greek means wisdom and it is wisdom he must attain before he can be united with Sophia and lead a contented and happy married life. In *Tom Jones*, this ideal is referred to by Squire Allworthy, sometimes as prudence and sometimes as discretion. A major theme of the novel is Tom's struggle to ward off the evil, licentious advances and move towards attaining a sound judgement. It is towards the end of the novel when Tom spurns the erotic offers of Mrs. Waters and Mrs. Fitzpatrick that he shows he has gained wisdom and restraint. He is now ready to gain Sophia, the symbol of wisdom itself.

Tom Jones and the Bible

Fielding draws several parallels between *Tom Jones* and the Bible. Tom resembles the Prodigal son whose story is told in Luke. Tom is an impetuous, wild young man lacking sexual restraint who is eventually reconciled and reunited with his father. The parallels with the story of Adam and Eve are more apparent. Allworthy's mansion is named 'Paradise Hall' from which Tom is banished. Even Sophia is forced to leave her country paradise in pursuit of Tom. Fielding compares Tom to Adam and quotes from Milton's *Paradise Lost*: "The world, as Milton phrases it, lay all before him, and Jones, no more than Adam, had any man to whom he might resort for comfort or assistance." In this way, he associates the country with Eden, in contrast to the harsh and hazardous road, which Tom and Sophia take to. Their return to the country is portrayed as the return to paradise, a metaphor for the happiness that love alone can bring.

15

Realism in *Tom Jones*

Realism is the reflection in literature of life itself. It aims at giving a truthful impression both of the tangible objects and the mental processes as they actually appear to the normal human consciousness without idealising them, sentimentalising them, or in any other way, distorting them through the experience of one's own preconceived ideas. A realist always tries to write from actual observation and experience and brings to his work a highly dispassionate mind and objective vision. As a rule, he excludes his own normative judgments or philosophical interpretations though it is always possible for a discerning reader to deduce from a work of art a set of values the writer might have liked to advocate, had he got the freedom of explicit statement.

Fielding, who is considered to be the pioneer of the realistic novel in England had a very intimate and variegated experience of life and he based all his writings on actual experience. How much importance he attached to actual experience is clear from his invocation to Experience in the prefatory chapter to Book XIII:

> Lastly, come Experience, long conversant with the wise, the good, the learned, and the polite. Nor with them only, but with every kind of character, from the minister at his levee, to the bailiff in his sponging-house; from the duchess at her drum, to the landlady behind her bar. From thee only can the manners of mankind be known; to which the recluse pedant, however great his pan. or extensive his learning may be, hath ever been a stranger.

With such an unqualified faith in actual experience, he copied, in his writings, from the Book of nature and scarcely produced a character or action which he had not taken from his own observation and experience. In his introduction to *Joseph Andrews,* he says:

> I believe I might aver that I have written little more than I have seen.

However, Harold Child has this pertinent remark to offer on Fielding's realism:

> If by a realist is meant an artist conscientiously determined to express life exactly as he sees it, then Fielding was one. But if a realist is one to whom all the facts of life and character, all aims and emotions are of equal value, Fielding cannot be called by that name. Fielding's realism

> unites the most common desires of the new society in England; the taste for the concrete, the need to see it without illusion in order not to feel any surprise or disappointment when acting upon it and co-operating with it, the resolution not to sacrifice the several elements of the human being one to another, and to know at times how to feel a soft emotion, when it is useful that the soul should be softened.

Fielding has followed the method of dramatic analysis in his novels. He has combined the act of creation with the act of judgment. Like a historian he undertakes to interpret and usually to make his own comments upon the matter in hand. He thus gives an intellectual account or interpretation of the facts of life, *i.e.* an ordered version of life in general rendering intelligible what was confused and obscure. Baker, therefore, calls Fielding's realism *intellectual realism.*

Realism in Characterisation

Fielding's knowledge of life and people was as extensive as that of Defoe while his insight was keener and deeper. In his early life he had come in intimate contact with the aristocracy. In his later life he studied the lower strata, while in his capacity of a magistrate, he got a very rare opportunity to have a close view of the working of the criminal mind. In *Tom Jones* Fielding gives a strictly veracious picture of the real human world he had so diligently observed and studied. He neither glosses over what is hideous and disgusting nor like Hogarth, Smollett or Thackeray omits what is pleasant and delightful. His characters are neither paragons of virtue nor monsters of vice but real human beings with their lights and shades in proper perspective, and he draws them with perfect honesty and candour. But he is not contented with the representation of mere external appearances of his characters. 'Go deeper than words', says he, 'and judge deeds; go deeper than deeds and judge intentions which are the immediate expression of the soul. Go deeper than even conscious intentions.' That is why Aurelien Digeon describes Fielding's realism as *psychological realism.* Fielding ruthlessly tears the mask of apparent reality and uncovers the essential reality. He exposes the rogue in the pious-looking Blifil, the hypocrite in the seemingly virtuous Square and the real gem of a man that to the world might be a rascally bastard born to be hanged. His Allworthy is benevolent but gullible; his Western is despotic but indulgent; his Tom is chivalrous but easily vulnerable. The self-opinionated Mrs. Western, the coquettish Molly and the debauched Lady Bellaston are definitely more alive than Richardson's Pamela or Clarissa. Saintsbury makes a very apt comparison between these two writers:

> In the novel as Richardson knew it and was thinking of it, when he began *Pamela,* you were, as a rule, in an artificial world altogether—a world artificial with an artificial only faintly and occasionally touched with any reality at all. In *Pamela* itself there is perhaps nothing, and certainly not

much, that is wholly unreal; but the reality is treated and rendered in an artificial way. In *Joseph Andrews,* though its professed genesis and procedure are artificial too, you break away at once from serious artifice. These are real people who do real things in a real way now as they did nearly two hundred years ago; however much dress, and speech, and manners may have changed. And we are told of their doing in a real way too.

Realistic Description of the Contemporary Life :

Fielding's portrayal of the eighteenth century life and manners in *Tom Jones* is so realistic that the novel can be accepted as an authentic social document. Its details are no less accurate than the statistical data available in the contemporary periodicals and journals. For example, Mrs. Calderwood's description of English roads as given in her *Journal* written in 1756, *i.e.* two years after Fielding's death conforms word for word with the one in *Tom Jones.* It is always so with Fielding. Moreover, he works on a very wide canvas and presents a panoramic view of the entire society. The poverty and squalour of the countryside along with the wealth and splendour, the poor condition of the highways with the sense of danger and insecurity felt by the travellers, the folly and frivolity of the fashionable society of London, and the growing materialism of the trading class have all been depicted with remarkable veracity. The inadequacy of public education, the deplorably poor professional knowledge of medical practitioners and the corruption and arbitrariness prevailing in law have also been well portrayed. The few references to the political activity are only incidental, but they suggest a period of political unrest and instability. The entire social life, of England comes alive in Fielding's portrayal of the country squires, innkeepers, barber-surgeons, gypsies, highwaymen, and of the rowdyism in the inns, the stage coaches, the puppet shows, the dramatic performances, the masquerades and the duels. It is the England of *Marriage a La Mode, The Harlot's Progress* and *The Rake's Progress,* the England of just before the Industrial Revolution. And so comprehensive and so accurate is Fielding's description of the life and manners of his age, that he appears to have embodied in his novel the very soul of his generation.

But Fielding was not merely the painter of his society; by implication, he was its critic also. He did not idealise his characters, nor did he select only the idealistic side of their life. But this does not mean that he did not cherish ideals or did not believe in them. A realistic picture of the mismanagement at an inn and the presence of rowdy and undesirable elements therein is in itself a plea for reform, better facilities and better atmosphere. To uphold and extort the correct values, to reflect life with a correct perspective, to enlarge one's understanding of life with a view to promoting a healthy outlook is an ideal every writer should emulate. By holding to ridicule the vanity and affectation of people, by exposing the malice, greed and selfishness and bringing retribution to those who practised them, Fielding makes amply clear the ideals he wanted his countrymen to pursue. He takes cognisance of the goodness of heart displayed by some and recommends it to all. He appreciates noble impulses and emphasises their importance in life. At other times, he depicts evil in all its ugliness and pleads for discretion and circumspection to avoid its snares. Fielding's pursuit of reality was never prompted by rancour or hatred, nor did it lead him to rejection or negation of life. Of all novelists, he is the one truly realistic.

Realism in the Structural Design of 'Tom Jones'

A brief comparison of *Tom Jones* with the eighteenth century romantic novel would illustrate a different kind of realism effected by Fielding. In a romantic novel, imagination is given a free rein. The narrative rambles along unexpected turns and twists. Probability of occurrence is violated to introduce cheap thrills and sensations. Some cheap, puerile comedy is inserted to produce fun. The characters are made to suffer abrupt reversals of fortune in order to make the piece sentimental. They are just robots in the hands of the novelist, who makes them dance to the requirements of the formula that governs the entire composition. But *Tom Jones* is free from this very common flaw. Its characters never appear to be under undue constraint. They follow their natural instincts; and yet their actions fall in such a neat and eye-catching pattern that the reader is just amazed at their happy contrivance. Even the coincidences in the novel are not made so improbable that they may shatter the impression of verisimilitude and strain one's credulity. Since the sequence of events at Upton is often criticised as 'highly contrived', let us analyse it to illustrate our point. The chief actors in this extremely exciting drama are Tom, Mrs. Waters, Partridge, Mr. Fitzpatrick, Sophia and Squire Western. What are their essential characteristics ? Tom is susceptible to women; Mrs. Waters is coquetish and easy of virtue. Partridge is loquacious and often talks irresponsibly. Mr. Fitzpatrick is rash and volatile. Sophia is sensitive; she can be magnanimous enough to forgive Tom his sexual levity but cannot stand her name being bandied about. Squire Western is violent and unrestrained. Isn't what happens at Upton a direct sequel to the personality traits listed above ? And yet doesn't the pattern of these events amaze us ? Doesn't it appear that neither the plot nor the character is allowed to dominate the other but a very satisfying harmony between the two is effected by the novelist. This kind of correspondence between the realism in characterisation and the realism in the occurrence of events is in evidence everywhere in *Tom Jones.* In fact the three most crucial events in the three different parts of the book, Tom's dismissal from Squire Allworthy's estate, the frustration of his love at Upton when so close to fulfilment, and his proposal of marriage to Lady Bellaston that antagonises her, all derive from his character.

Conclusion

Richardson once accused Fielding that 'his brawls, his jars, his gaols, his sponging-houses are all drawn from what he has seen and known'. Poor Richardson ! he did not know that there could not be a better compliment to Fielding's realistic portrayals than this accusation.

16

Fielding's Style in *Tom Jones*

Fielding is as much praised for the spontaneity, naturalness and vigour of his style as for the architectonic qualities of his plot construction or the perceptive portrayal of his characters. He is equally at ease whether his style is plain and homely or majestic and dignified. He can be familiar, ironical, satirical or poetic at will and nowhere does his style give the impression of being laboured and affected. Tennyson refers to Fielding as the 'lord of the language'. George Eliot also talks of the 'lusty ease of Fielding's fine English'. But perhaps the finest encomium comes from Andrew Lang:

> There is somewhat inexpressibly heartening to me in the style of Fielding. One seems to be carried along, like a swimmer in a strong, clear stream, trusting oneself to every whirl and eddy, with a feeling of safety, of comfort, or delightful ease in the motion of the elastic water.

Variety of Fielding's Style

Fielding can successfully vary his style to suit his subject. He is in such a perfect control of his medium that he can use the same panegyric style to betray the insincerity of sentiment as well as to express its seriousness. In Book XV, chapter 5, Lord Fellamar addresses Sophia

> ....love hath so totally deprived me of reason, that I am scarce accountable for any of my actions.......I dote on you to the highest degree of distraction. O most adorable, most divine creature ! what language can express the sentiments of my heart ?

And in Book XVI, chapter 3, Tom Jones writes to Sophia

> Can the most perfect admiration, the most watchful observance, the most ardent love, the most melting tenderness, the most resigned submission to your will, make you amends for what you are to sacrifice to my happiness ? If they can, fly, my lovely angel, to those arms which are ever open to receive and protect you; and to which, whether you bring yourself alone, or the riches of the world with you, is, in my opinion, an alternative not worth regarding......

In spite of the elevated style, simple words like *dote* and *distract* betray the lustfulness of Lord Fellamar whereas Tom's letter is aglow with the sincerity and sanctity of his sentiment.

Pervasive Use of Open Irony

One of the most conspicuous characteristics of Fielding's style is his pervasive use of open irony. Fielding's irony makes the fact of dissimulation definitely more obvious than say the irony of Defoe or Swift. Swift's irony is subtler but when its intended meaning is revealed, the sarcasm hidden in it cuts one to the quick and leaves one stunned. Fielding's irony is much lighter in tone. It is mild and tolerant. We get a taste of Fielding's irony as early as Book I, chapter 2, when he introduces to us Miss Bridget Allworthy:

> ....She was of that species of women whom you commend rather for good qualities than beauty, and who are generally called, by their own sex, very good sort of women—as good a sort of women, madam, as you wish to know. Indeed, she was so far from regretting want of beauty, that she never mentioned that perfection, if it can be called one, without contempt; and would often thank God she was not as handsome as Miss Such-a-one, whom perhaps beauty had led into errors, which she might have otherwise avoided.

Here very ironically, Fielding presents to us the delusion of an ugly spinster who believes that lack of beauty is a virtue and beauty is only a snare, hence it deserves contempt. It should be noted that the presentation of Bridget's delusion is not direct, for Fielding seems to be presenting Bridget's own point of view. This irony exposes Bridget's delusion and lightly ridicules it, without being unduly harsh. Fielding's penchant for open irony gives one the feeling that he has a very open, forthright mind that does not believe in mincing matters. Occasionally, Fielding makes his irony a bit too emphatic and obvious also, and hence undermines its subtlety, but usually he employs it quite skilfully and effectively.

The Mock-heroic

An important aspect of Fielding's irony is his use of the deliberately inflated style and the mock-heroic. The deliberately inflated style is used casually and only in brief descriptions. But when this style is persisted with and the fact that it is the parody of some genuinely elevated style becomes a bit too obvious, it may be called the mock-heroic. Most notable examples of the mock-heroic style are Molly Seagrim's battle in the churchyard with her envious neighbours, the battle at the Upton Inn and Mrs. Waters's seduction of Tom Jones in Book IX. Dudden quotes Lord Monboddo to raise two objections to the use of the mock-heroic:

> ....they make too great a change of style, being as it were, gaudy patches on what is otherwise simple and familiar; ....they impair the probability of the narrative which ought to be carefully studied in all works that are imitations of real life and manners.

The objections are not totally out of place. But Fielding accepted the deliberate use of the burlesque as a part of his theory of the novel as a comic epic in prose. He used the mock-heroic for a variety of purposes: to emphasise the triviality of the situation and to exhibit the stupidity and ridiculousness inherent in it; to use it as a kind of poetic embellishment for the enlivenment of the novel; to introduce variety into his style and break its monotony; and finally, to produce some pure comedy.

Descriptions in an Adorned Style followed by Descriptions in a Very Plain Style

A rather curious feature of Fielding's style is to give a description in a highly adorned style and then to repeat it in plain English introducing it with such phrases as 'in a word', 'in vulgar phrase', etc. In Book IX, chapter 3, Fielding is about to describe Tom's battle with the landlady at the Upton Inn. The landlady arms herself with some very effective weapon:

> ....she had provided herself with a long deadly instrument, with which, in times of peace, the chambermaid was wont to demolish the labours of the industrious spider.

This description is immediately followed by the following sentence:

> In vulgar phrase, she had taken up the broomstick........

Similarly in Book I, chapter 13, there is a description of Captain Blifil's treatment of his brother:

> One of the maxims which the devil, in a late visit upon earth, left to his disciples, is, when once you are got up, to kick the stool from under you.

This is immediately followed by the following sentence:

> In plain English, when you have made your fortune by the good offices of a friend, you are advised to discard him as soon as you can.

Ian Watt writes of the double audience which Fielding and his contemporaries addressed—the ordinary reader and the learned man, the audience that had a taste for nothing but the plain and the homely and the audience that was well-groomed in classical heritage and had sufficient intellectual training to enjoy the poetic flavour of an embellished style. It appears that Fielding was trying to cater to both kinds of his audience.

Fondness For Archaic Forms

Apart from these, there are a few other characteristics of Fielding's style also. Fielding is very fond of the archaic forms like *doth* and *hath.* Practically all of Fielding's contemporaries showed a preference for the modern forms *does* and *has.* But in Fielding, these obsolescent locutions are used, quite consistently and habitually.

Literary Allusions

Secondly, Fielding has a predilection for using literary allusions. It reminds us that Fielding had an extremely sound education of the classics, sound even by the eighteenth century standards. These literary allusions and quotations come to him quite naturally and he uses them felicitously. He neither labours nor dwells on them too long to justify Thackeray's censure that Fielding makes an absurd brag of his two-penny learning. Fielding's learning is both solid and comprehensive and he never brags of it.

Effective Use of Dialogues

Fielding makes a very effective use of dialogues. He uses dialogues both to advance the narrative and to create and substantiate the characters. Fielding commands a great range in the writing of dialogues. Whether it is the measured utterance of Squire Allworthy, the rustic vulgarity and vociferation of Squire Western, the comic loquacity and pedantry of Partridge, the hollow, grandiloquent reflections of Square, the sentimental garrulity of Mrs. Miller, the sober and pious hypocrisy of Blifil, the business parlance of the old Nightingale, Fielding is equally convincing in all of them. His genius appears to be failing him only when he has to communicate the intensity of emotions. There seems to be a touch of the affected in a passage like Tom's soliloquy in Book V, chapter 10:

> O Sophia, would Heaven give thee to my arms, how blest would be my condition ! Curst be that fortune which sets a distance between us. Was I but possessed of thee, one only suit of rags thy whole estate, is there a man on earth whom I would envy ! How contemptible would the brightest Circassian beauty, dressed in all the jewels of the Indies, appear to my eyes !

Fielding is a great master when he has to display the irony inherent in a situation and transform it into apt material for rich comedy, but he appears to be handicapped when he has to deficit the depth of feeling in a genuinely touching moment (When Tom beseeches Sophia not to marry Blifil) or a really sentimental snatch of conversation (When Mrs. Miller describes the woes of the Andersons).

17

The Mock-heroic in *Tom Jones*

Mock-heroic as an Essential Aspect of Fielding's Style

The mock-heroic is a style which consciously parodies the style of epic or heroic poetry. Fielding's concept of the novel being a comic epic in prose, he should naturally be expected to burlesque the style of an epic. He often employs a deliberately inflated mode of description to reveal the hidden irony in a situation. But his style becomes truly mock-heroic when this inflation is sustained and forces upon the reader an awareness of some unburlesqued original, say Homer's style in *The Iliad* that is genuinely elevated.

Epic Similes

Fielding appears to have a weakness for epic similes. For example, in Book I, chapter 6, Mrs. Deborah Wilkins is introduced into the parish with an epic simile. Fielding writes:

> Not otherwise than when a kite, tremendous bird, is beheld by the feathered generation soaring aloft, and hovering over their heads, the amorous dove, and every innocent little bird, spread wide the alarm, and fly trembling to their hiding-places. He proudly beats the air, conscious of his dignity, and meditates intended mischief.

Then he goes on to explain the situation in plain language:

> The sagacious reader will not from this simile imagine these poor people had any apprehension of the design with which Mrs. Wilkins was now coming towards them; but as the great beauty of the simile may possibly sleep these hundred years, till some future commentator shall take this work in hand, I think proper to lend the reader a little assistance in this place.
>
> It is my intention, therefore, to signify, that, as it is the nature of a kite to devour little birds, so it is the nature of such persons as Mrs. Wilkins to insult and tyrannise over little people,

Again, when in Book II, chapter 6, Mrs. Patridge suspects her husband of infidelity and launches a bloody assault, she is mock heroically compared to a cat and Partridge himself to a mouse. Mrs. Partridge's description goes as follows:

> As fair Grimalkin, who, though the youngest of the feline family, degenerates not in ferocity from the elder branches

> of her house, and though inferior in strength, is equal in fierceness to the noble tiger himself, when a little mouse whom it hath long tormented in sport, escapes from her clutches for a while, frets, scolds, growls, swears; but if the trunk, or box, behind which the mouse lay hid be again removed, she flies like lightning on her prey, and, with envenomed wrath, bites, scratches, mumbles, and tears the little animal.

There follows in the next paragraph the description of the actual occurrence in a plain, deflated style:

> Not with less fury did Mrs. Partridge fly on the poor pedagogue. Her tongue, teeth, and hands fell all upon him at once. His wig was in an instant torn from his head, his shirt from his back, and from face descended five streams of blood, denoting the number of claws with which nature had unhappily armed the enemy.

Even more elaborate is the mock-heroic preliminary to the discovery of Tom by Thwackum and Blifil in the bushes with Molly Seagrim in Book V, chapter 11. The chapter title itself is in the mock-heroic style: In which a simile in Mr. Pope's period of a mile introduces as bloody a battle as can possibly be fought without the assistance of steel or cold iron.

The Mock-heroic Style: Molly Seagrim's Battle in the Churchyard

But the real taste of the mock-heroic is found in those episodes where the parody of the epic style is sustained throughout. Such a one is Molly Seagrim's battle in the churchyard with her envious neighbours in book IV, chapter 8. The chapter is titled: A battle sung by the Muse in the Homerican style, and which none but the classical reader can taste. Fielding begins with an invocation to the Muse:

> Ye Muses, then, whoever ye are, who love to sing battles, and principally thou who whilom didst recount the slaughter in those fields where Yudibras and Trulla fought, if thou were not starved with thy friend Butler, assist me on this great occasion. All things are not in the power of all.

Then he proceeds with an epic simile (choosing, of course, a very ludicrous comparison):

> As a vast herd of cows in a rich farmer's yard, if, while they are milked, they hear their calves at a distance, lamenting the robbery which is then committing, roar and bellow, so roared forth the Somersetshire mob...

This seems to be quite like a simile drawn from *The Iliad* in the genuine, Homeric elevated style. Going on with the parody, Fielding begins to recount the names of the victims of Molly's fury:

> Recount, O Muse, the names of those who fell on this fatal day. First, Jemmy Tweedle felt on his hinder head the direful bone. Him the pleasant banks of sweetly-winded Stour had nourished where he first learnt the vocal art, with which, wandering up and down at wakes and fairs, he cheered the rural nymphs and swains when upon the green they interweaved the sprightly dance; while he himself stood riddling and jumping to his own music. How little now avails his fiddle ! He thumps the verdant floor with this carcass. Next, old Echepole, the sowgelder......

This parodies the Homeric technique of listing heroes in their fall and recounting something of their earlier history.

Described in a similar vein is the battle at Upton in Book IX, chapter 3.

Mrs. Waters's Seduction of Tom Jones

Perhaps the best example of the mock-heroic style is Mrs. Waters's seduction of Tom Jones in Book IX, chapter 5. The very title of the chapter suggests mischief: An apology for all heroes who have good stomachs, with a description of a battle of the amorous kind. The beginning of the chapter is marked with deceptive sobriety in which Fielding shows how even the heroes suffer the pangs of hunger like everyone else. 'This opening has a triple purpose: it reduces the hero to the level of ordinary man and thus is in itself anti-heroic; it introduces the subject of food which is to be playful alternative to love in the encounter to follow; it is a feint for the central matter of this chapter is not food but love.'

Tom Jones and Mrs. Waters sit down at a meal with Tom having eyes for nothing but beef and ale, and Mrs. Waters playing all her 'artillery' upon him. Fielding again begins with an invocation:

> Say then, ye Graces ! you that inhabit the heavenly mansions of Seraphina's countenance; for you are truly divine, are always in her presence, and well know all the arts of charming; say, what were the weapons now used to captivate the heart of Mr. Jones.

Then Fielding proceeds with a minute description of this amorous battle:—

> First, from two lovely blue eyes, whose bright orbs flashed lightning at their discharge, flew forth two pointed ogles; but, happily for our hero, hit only a vast piece of beef which he was then conveying into his plate, and harmless spent their force. The fair warrior perceived their miscarriage, and immediately from her fair bosom drew forth a deadly sigh. A sigh which none could have heard unmoved, and which was sufficient at once to have swept *off a* dozen beaus; so soft, so sweet, so tender, that the insinuating air

must have found its subtle way to that heart of our hero, had it not unluckily been driven from his ears by the coarse bubbling of some bottle ale, which at that time he was pouring forth. Many other weapons did she assay; but the god of eating (if there be any such deity, for I do not confidently assert it) preserved his votary; or perhaps it may not be *dignus vindice nodus,* and the present security of Jones may be accounted for by natural means; for as love frequently preserves from the attacks of hunger, so may hunger possibly, in some cases, defend us against love.

18

Humour in *Tom Jones*

Humour a Part of Fielding's Conception of the Novel as a 'Comic Epic in Prose'

Fielding has conceived *Tom Jones* as a comic epic in prose. In the preface to *Joseph Andrews,* he observes that a comic epic employs 'light and ridiculous' fable and action and in its sentiments and diction, it preserves the ludicrous. Thus humour occupies a very prominent place in Fielding's very conception of the novel. In the same preface, he also traces the source of this humour. Humour springs from the ridiculous and the only source of the true Ridiculous is affectation. Affectation proceeds from either vanity or hypocrisy. We affect vanity in order to purchase applause whereas hypocrisy aims at the avoidance of censure. Vanity is ostentation; hypocrisy, deceit. Affectation arising from either vanity or hypocrisy provokes derision. Fielding holds affectation to ridicule obviously with a view to correcting humanity of its follies. He reiterates this purpose in his dedication to *Tom Jones.*

> I have employed all the wit and humour of which I am master in the following history; wherein I have endeavoured to laugh mankind out of their favourite follies and vices.

Again, in his invocation to Genius, he says:

> Come, thou who hast inspired thy Aristophanes, thy Lucian, thy Cervantes, thy Rabelais, thy Moliere, thy Shakespeare, thy Swift, thy Marivaux, fill my pages with humour till mankind learn the good nature to laugh only at the follies of others and the humility to grieve at their own.

This is a very solemn purpose indeed and quite in accord with his epic theory of the novel, and he mostly uses ironical or satirical humour to achieve this purpose. But though he never loses sight of this purpose, he is not always preoccupied with it also. He is endowed with a very sanguine temperament and takes delight in fun for its own sake, fun that is just farcical and has no ulterior motive. Thus, in Fielding, humour may be of three varieties; farcical, ironical and satirical.

Farcical Humour

It is *Joseph Andrews* that abounds in gay, farcical humour. Fielding appears to have matured and mellowed while writing *Tom Jones.* Now his buoyancy is restrained and there is much less of buffoonery and horseplay, but it is not totally absent. There is the assault on Partridge by his 'Amazonian' wife, or the 'epic' fight between Molly and the offended congregation at the church, a fight at which the village clowns and hoydens burlesque the gallant feats of the Homeric heroes, or the fray at the Upton Inn where fists, cudjels and broomsticks are employed most freely, but the most effective weapon used is the tongue that lashes so mercilessly. In the same class are the naive, unsophisticated comments made by Partridge on Garrick's performance of *Hamlet* in London or his most comic interruptions of the story narrated by the Man of the Hill. A good deal of coarse and vulgar material goes into the production of this kind of humour, but the humour itself is untainted with vulgarity. The episodes employing farcical humour offer fine examples of 'writing upon low subjects without writing in a low manner'. Byron, too, referring to this vulgarity, observes:

> It does not depend upon low themes or even low language, for Fielding revels in both; but is he ever vulgar ? No. You see the man of education, the gentleman and the scholar, sporting with his subject—its master, not its slave.

Ironical Humour

It Joseph Andrews abounds in farcical humour and *Jonathan Wild* in satirical humour, it is ironical humour that is chiefly affected in *Tom Jones.* A light and gentle irony is diffused throughout the novel. There is the scene in Molly's bed room. Molly, with tears streaming down her cheeks and her voice choked makes loud protestations of her love for Tom and swears that she can never live without him, when suddenly the rug curtain falls to disclose, in a very undignified posture, the grave philosopher Square, the professed champion of 'the unalterable rule of right and the eternal fitness of things'. This is an ironical comment both on Molly and on Square and it achieves its purpose without causing much bitterness. Then there is Captain Blifil who; though himself in league with Bridget, tries to convince Squire Allworthy of the propriety of punishing bastard children for the sins of their parents or who uses a discourse on Christian charity as an occasion for giving a damaging information against a man who has never done him any harm. 'Bridget who is condemned to a wretched existence with her husband appears 'inconsolable' after his death and raises a laudatory epitaph in his memory. Blifil makes an appeal to the most cherished Christian doctrines of liberty and mercy to release the bird with the wickedest motives in mind. After Squire Allworthy's recovery, Tom meditates most piously on the charms of Sophia and declares that nothing but Sophia's fair bosom could give him any solace, but only minutes later, retires into a thicket with Molly. The Man of the Hill is rescued by Tom from a violent assault by a pack of ruffians but the very next morning, he prevails upon Tom to show no concern for a woman's shrieks. There are hardly any chapters in *Tom Jones* that do not provide examples of this kind of humour. Irony sometimes overflows even into the chapter headings. Thus the chapter dealing with the death of Captain Blifil is given the title: A Receipt to regain the lost Affection of a Wife.

Ironical humour can either be sportive and tolerant or scathing and relentless The latter type is found mainly in *Jonathan Wild.* Irony in *Tom Jones* is mostly mild and humane; it criticises through exposure but does not condemn. Fielding has the true humorist's tolerance of human weaknesses. He knows that human beings can be foolish without being wicked, so their indiscretions might be subjected to good-natured raillery and banter but not to offensive laceration of feelings.

Satirical Humour

Quite expectedly, Fielding does not indulge much in satirical humour. But whatever little of satire is employed by him is very different in tone from the stern and scathing satire of Swift. Satire often uses invective and vituperation. But invective offends and arouses indignation. The subject of an invective instead of regretting his own moral lapses is likely to retaliate in the most ungainly manner. So, Fielding, very discreetly, refrains from castigating individuals and directs his satirical humour against groups and classes—parsons and doctors, beaus and booby squires, wailing maids and fine ladies, Methodists and Jacobites. Secondly, he produces satirical humour at the cost of the manners and morals of the contemporary society in general and even humanity at large.

Humour through Parody, Depiction of Incongruities, etc.; Humour in Situation, Humour in Characterisation

Apart from irony and satire, Fielding uses various other methods to produce humour. At Upton Inn, Tom is subjected to a mock trial and Fielding gives a nonsensical but delightful parody of the technical jargon of lawyers. Often Fielding surprises his readers by some ridiculous incongruity. Squire Allworthy delivers a fine death-bed valediction to his household though all the while he is suffering from nothing worse than feverish cold. Another method to produce humour is to bring together two diametrically opposite types of characters such as Thwackum and Square and to involve them in a boisterous wrangle. Some humour is produced through ludicrous misunderstanding as when Sophia and her aunt discuss a person who would be acceptable to them as Sophia's lover, each mistakenly imagining that they are speaking of the same person, or through deliberate pretence as when Tom, Sophia and Lady Bellaston accidentally come together at the Lady' residence and pretend that they are totally unacquainted with one another. Sometimes Fielding contrives ridiculous but highly amusing situations. In Mrs. Miller's apartments in London, Mrs. Honour lashes at Lady Bellaston's unabashed licentiousness in most unkind words with the Lady herself hidden behind the curtain. Only a few scenes later, lady Bellaston's repugnant wooing of Tom is abruptly interrupted by the arrival of Nightingale in a drunken state; the Lady, scared and confused, tries to hide behind the curtain only to discover that Mrs. Honour is already lodged there. But Fielding excels most in providing humour of character. Parson Adams in *Joseph Andrews* is of course the finest example of this type of humour. Adams, with his absent-mindedness, his small pedantries, his naive trust in human goodness which is always being betrayed, produces much fun in the novel. Conceived almost in the same mould are Squire Western and Partridge. Squire Western showers rhapsodic affection on his daughter at one moment and at the very next, he takes recourse to oaths and threats in order to persuade her to accept a match of his own choice. He is so frantically chasing his daughter and is almost on the verge of overtaking her when he gives up the chase just because it is such a fine day for hunting. Partridge also is a purely comic character who arouses much laughter with his artless naivete.

Humour is Exuberant, Spontaneous, Tolerant and Exercised on Realities

Finally, Fielding's humour in *Tom Jones* is distinguished by four qualities. It is amazingly exuberant. Fielding is a born humorist and the fountain of his mirth is never exhausted. He is gifted with a remarkably fecund imagination and can contrive an immense variety of humorous situations. Secondly, his humour is highly spontaneous. It plays lightly and naturally without any suggestion of premeditation or deliberate contrivance. Thirdly, it is tolerant and benign. Fielding does not, of course, condone the moral lapses of his characters, still he takes a very lenient view of them. Fourthly it is exercised on realities, on the facts of nature and life, and not on whims and fancies.

19

Tom Jones as a Picaresque Novel

What is a Picaresque Novel ?

The term *picaresque* has been derived from a Spanish word *picaro* which means a rogue or a villain. Originally, a type of romance that dealt with rogues or villains was called picaresque. A picaresque novel presented, in an extravagant style, a series of adventures and misadventures, mostly on the highways. Some more enterprising novelists sent their hero to the sea also. With the development of the novel, it was no longer considered essential to take only a rogue or a villain as the central character. A regular hero, gallant and chivalric, adventurous in spirit and liberal in out-look, came to be equally acceptable.

The picaresque form offered many advantages to the novelist. It did not require a regular, well-organised, well-rounded plot. The novelist could afford to dispense with the episodical unity and just contrive a succession of sensational events involving his chief protagonist. Secondly he got an opportunity to introduce a wide variety of events and characters. The hero is now in the country, now on the highways, now in London, confronting thieves, grappling with rogues, rescuing beautiful damsels and falling in love, fighting duels, getting arrested and languishing in prison, getting robbed by the most innocent looking people and helped by those who looked scoundrels, getting intimately in touch with a vast variety of people from the country squires to the haughty and rakish aristocrats, from the boorish and nagging landladies to the morose and ill-tempered military personnel, from hypocrites and imposters to gypsies and fiddlers. Finally, the picaresque form offered enough scope to throw light on the life, culture and morality of the age and to criticise the evils infesting it. The earliest examples of the picaresque novel are *Lazaritle de Tonnes* and *Guzman de Alfarachi.* Le Sage's *Gil Bias* is the most well-known picaresque novel in French and Cervante's *Don Quixote* in Spanish. In English, Defoe wrote in the picaresque tradition. Later, Fielding in *Joseph Andrews* and *Tom Jones* and Smollett in his novels of sea adventure like *Roderick Random* followed the same tradition. The traces of this tradition are found even in Dickens and Thackeray.

'Tom Jones' as a Picaresque Novel

Tom Jones is not a regular picaresque novel. But it incorporates in its structure the major characteristics of the picaresque form. The first six Books depict Tom's adventures in the countryside. The poaching incident, Molly's battle in the churchyard, Tom's escapade with Molly in the bushes are all in the picaresque tradition. But strictly speaking, it is with Book VII when, dismissed by Squire Airworthy, Tom takes the road to Bristol, that the really picaresque nature of the novel becomes evident. Henceforward, for the next six Books, Tom is involved in some breath-taking, swashing adventures on the roadside. In Book VII, piqued by some scurrilous jests at Sophia's expense by Ensign Northerton, Tom picks a quarrel with him and gets hit on the head with a bottle of wine. In this very Book, following Cervante's example, Fielding provides Tom with an English counterpart of Sancho Panza—the pedantic-garrulous-cowardly Partridge. As if it were not enough to bring only the hero to the highways, even Sophia and Mrs. Honour are put on the road to London. Tom's next halt is at the Bell, which he is forced to leave on account of the rude and insulting behaviour of the landlady, though it is five o'clock in midwinter and the cowardly Partridge is little inclined to give up the security of the inn. The same evening, he rescues the Man of the Hill from being robbed by two ruffians and the next morning, he saves Mrs. Waters from being strangled by Ensign Northerton. After a night's stay at the Upton Inn, where some hilarious comedy takes place, Tom is again on the roadside now to meet beggars, highwaymen and gypsies. Fielding finds an opportunity even to insert a puppet show. In London itself, there is a masquerade, an attempted rape with a timely rescue, an intrigue followed by a ghastly duel and the arrest of Tom and the final resolution.

The picaresque nature of the novel enables Fielding to bring his hero in contact with different strata of the society—country squires, divines and philosophers, lawyers and military officers, landladies, beggars and highwaymen, gypsies, and finally the aristocrats—and expose the contemporary social evils as well as human follies and foibles of a more general nature. Among these, the worldly-minded priests and the corrupt aristocrats seem to have aroused him to the maximum indignation. General human weaknesses that Fielding holds to ridicule are the envy, malice, selfishness and hypocrisy of saintlike figures who are held in high esteem, figures like Square, Thwackum and Blifil.

Tom Jones does not follow the picaresque tradition inasmuch as its narrative is nowhere rambling or discursive. In fact, it offers one of the finest examples of an organically growing plot. Its adventures are not arbitrarily designed and inserted to adorn the narrative. Their incidence derives from the character of the hero and their course is not totally unpredictable.

20
Prefatory Chapters in *Tom Jones*

Fielding begins each of the Books in *Tom Jones* with a prefatory essay which has no connection with the novel itself. These essays occasionally occur in other novels also, but in *Tom Jones* they are a regular feature. Fielding tells us that he took great pains in writing them. He observes:

> I can with less pains write one of the books of the history than the prefatory chapter to each of them.

These prefatory chapters may be compared to the prologue of a play. At first these prologues were an integral part of the play, but now they are used to serve some purpose of the dramatist himself. Fielding agrees that these initial chapters may as properly be prefixed to any other Book in this history, or indeed to any other history as to this. Indeed, they may be altogether dropped, without any injury to the narrative, although they would substantially reduce the pleasure of some discriminating readers. Sir Walter Scott derived much pleasure from reading them:

> Those critical introductions, which rather interrupt the course of the story and the flow of the interest at the first perusal, are found on a second or third the most entertaining chapters of the whole work.

In these initial essays, Fielding has expressed some of his views on art, literature and life. These essays contain the views of the father of the English novel on novel in particular and life and literature in general; hence they are of abiding interest for a student of literature.

The Subject of the Novel: Human Nature

Fielding compares a novelist to an inn-keeper. Just as an innkeeper provides his guests with a bill of fare, the novelist ought to inform his readers of the subject of the novel. Fielding says that his *bill of fare* is *human nature*—a subject of such prodigious variety as would be difficult to exhaust.

One may dismiss this subject as just commonplace, for this is precisely the subject of all the romances, novels, plays and poems. But it is not a valid objection. How good a dish is depends upon how well it has been prepared. Human nature in the hands of an author deficient in wit, taste and learning may not resemble human nature at all.

It is obvious that in the context of his own novel, Fielding would like to be judged by the standards of truth. He would like his readers to appeal to their own knowledge of human nature in order to commend or censure his creation.

This subject, human nature, has to be made presentable to the reader. For this, Fielding makes use of two principles. The first is the principle of selection. According to this, the novelist must not follow the method of a 'painful and voluminous historian' who records all incidents of human affairs, whether or not they have any significance in the context of the theme of the novel. The novelist should take pains to exclude all extraneous matter and record only what is significant. If nothing eventful takes place, he may skip over whole years in silence; on the other hand, he should treat at length any happening of exceptional significance or interest. The second principle is that of lively and varied presentation. A plain record of facts and events might be dull and boring; hence the novelist should use 'sundry similes, descriptions, and other kinds of poetic embellishments' which might help to refresh the reader's mind and sustain his interest.

Of Critics

Fielding does not appear to have much regards for the critic. He believes that every work of art follows its own particular laws for its organic growth and it would be imprudence to lay down any dogmatic laws. But that is what the critics presume to do. According to Fielding, critics are men of shallow genius, who mistake mere form for the substance.

Fielding draws a distinction between the true critic such as Aristotle, Horace, Longinus and the false one who should better be called a slanderer. A good critic gives accurate judgment; a slanderer simply condemns. So bitter is Fielding, indeed, towards indiscreet condemnation that he actually equates it with murder.

Fielding also objects to certain defamatory terms used by some critics without properly knowing their significance. Fielding, in particular, points out the reckless use of the word *low* for what is commonplace and natural. Fielding asserts that in a good novel, which is nothing but a realistic picture of human life and character, both the commonplace and the extraordinary have to be delineated side by side.

Of Love

Fielding is exasperated at the many misconceptions prevalent about love. But he is quite clear-headed himself. He allows that there are a few persons, mostly philosophers, deficient in the passion of love. Others confuse it with lust, which should, more appropriately, be called hunger. The love that Fielding advocates satisfies him in a much more delicate manner although it seeks its own satisfaction as much as 'the grossest of all our appetites'. This love, when it operates towards one of the opposite sex is not mere hunger though it includes in it that hunger. Hunger in this case heightens all delights of love.

Love, according to Fielding, is a kind and benevolent disposition which gratifies itself by contributing to the happiness of others. The pleasures of pure love may be heightened by amorous desires but can exist without them.

Of Human Weaknesses

Fielding is quite tolerant of human weakness. According to him someone occasionally guilty of a natural weakness is not essentially bad. This world is often compared to a stage. The actors who play evil roles on the stage are not necessarily wicked in their actual life. Similarly, those who sometimes perform evil deeds are not necessarily bad characters. Hence any indiscriminate condemnation of persons should be avoided. Fielding says:

> The man of candour and of true understanding is never hasty to condemn. He can censure an imperfection, or even a vice, without rage against the guilty party.

Fielding would like us to understand that a fault or two that might be either congenital or begotten by certain evil influences and hence, probably, beyond perfect control, should not be fatally detrimental to one's value as a human being:

> The finest composition of human nature, as well as, the finest china may have a fault in it; and this I am afraid, in either case is equally incurable; though nevertheless, the pattern may remain of the highest value.

Law of Credibility in the Novel

In order to ensure credibility in the novel, Fielding lays down three laws for a practising novelist. The first is the rule of possibility. Nothing beyond the range of human capacity should be related in the novel. Miracles should be avoided. Supernatural agency should not be allowed to interfere with the story. In shaping his narrative a novelist should scrupulously follow the law of cause and effect.

The second is the rule of probability. Improbable things do happen in real life but rarely. Hence they should better be avoided. Even an exceptionally good or bad character should not be included for it would strain credulity. There shouldn't, also, be given improbable turns and twists to characters. Fielding is highly critical of the dramatists of his age whose heroes are notorious bawds and rakes for the first four acts but suddenly transform into worthy and respectable gentlemen in the fifth.

A strict observance of the rules of possibility and probability, however, does not inhibit the novelist 'from showing many persons and things which may possibly have never fallen within the knowledge of great part of his readers'. He is entitled at least to some faith from his readers.

According to the third rule, the actions should not only be possible and probable within the compass of human nature but also be consistent with the character of the performer. Fielding remarks:

> I will venture to say, that for a man to act in direct contradiction to the dictates of his nature, is, if not

> impossible, as improbable and as miraculous as anything which can well be conceived.

Four Major Qualifications of a Novelist

Fielding says that writing well demands the exercise of some very rare talent. Then he goes on to define this talent as consisting of *genius, learning, conversation* and *sensibility. Genius* is nothing but the twin qualities, *invention* and *judgment. Invention* implies the faculty of penetrating into the real essence of all things we observe and contemplate. *Judgment* means the faculty of discriminating between things. *Genius* is absolutely necessary for a correct portrayal of human life and human character.

Learning is the mental equipment that makes *invention* and *judgment* perfect for the use of a novelist. It helps to sharpen these natural gifts. Fielding considers a competent knowledge of history and of the works of other renowned literary artists very essential for a novelist.

Conversation implies personal experience of men and women. It 'means a regular intercourse not with one particular rank or class of men and women but with all ranks and classes.

Finally, a novelist must have *sensibility,* the capacity to feel. It means the power of placing oneself in the position of others and realising their joys and sorrows. Fielding's comments are:

> The author who will make me weep, says Horace, must first weep himself. In reality, no man can paint a distress well which he doth not feel while he is painting it; nor do I doubt, but that the most pathetic and affecting scenes have been writ with tears. In the same manner it is with the ridicules. I am convinced I never make my reader laugh heartily but where I have laughed before him.......

Of Plagiarism

Fielding allows the modern writer the liberty to borrow anything good from the great classical writers. Perhaps he feels that they belong to all. But he deems it a crime to borrow from one another without acknowledgement. That would be stealing. He declares that if ever he borrows from a contemporary, he will acknowledge credit where credit is due.

Of Aristocracy

Fielding believed that the members of aristocracy were elegant and refined, and possessed a 'liberality of spirit' that was scarcely ever seen in 'men of low birth and education', but their politeness or refinement was mostly an affectation. Fielding says:

> I will venture to say the highest life is much the dullest, and affords very little humour or entertainment.......here, except

> among the few who are engaged in the pursuit of ambition, and the fewer still who have a relish of pleasure, all is vanity and servile imitation. Dressing and cards, eating and drinking, bowing and courtesying make up the business of their lives.

However, Fielding believed that his contemporary high society was less lewd but more foolish:

> In my humble opinion, the characteristic of the present beau monde is rather folly than vice, and the only epithet which it deserves is that of frivolous.

21

Fielding's Contribution to the Development of the English Novel

It is true that even before Fielding, Defoe and Richardson had written novels, but it is with Fielding only that the novel gets its proper shape. He made invaluable contribution to the development of plot construction and the art of characterisation and explored the hidden potentialities of this genre as an art form. He bade farewell to the fantastic world of romance and firmly planted the novel in his own soil making it an effective weapon of social criticism. He also tried to advocate a healthy philosophy of life and thus imbued his writings with a very solemn purpose.

Plot Construction

Plot before Fielding did not hold much importance for the novelist. Bunyan's plots were only an apology to indulge in long, exhausting, theological digressions. Defoe's plots were mechanical, loose and episodic. Richardson worked on very flimsy plots. Dr. Johnson was right in his estimate that if anyone read Richardson for the story, his patience would be so much fretted that he would hang himself. But Fielding employs very coherent and organic plots and conducts them with utmost skill. Sir Walter Scott is known to have greatly admired in *Tom Jones* 'the felicitous contrivance, and happy extrication of the story, where every incident tells upon and advances the catastrophe' while, at the same time, it illustrates the characters of those interested in its approach'. As one reads along, one is deeply impressed by Fielding's inventiveness and the fecundity of his imagination, but it is only at the conclusion that one realises that the various episodes were not meant to embellish the narrative; they were relevant in their context. The excellence of Fielding's plots can be summed up best by saying that they are thoroughly 'architechtonic'. Thackeray describes Fielding's work as 'literary providence' and Coleridge records his enthusiasm for the plot of *Tom Jones* by saying that it is one of the three best plots ever planned. A well-organised plot appears to be the main contribution of Fielding according to Walter Allen:

> In the end what we are conscious of in *Tom Jones* over and above Fielding's sheer exuberance of creation is the form of a novel as a work designed and shaped. The realisation of form and shape in this sense is one of the greatest pleasures we can get from any work of art.

Novel as a Comic Epic in Prose

Another contribution of Fielding is his concept of the novel as *a comic epic in prose.* He invented a fable as wide in its canvas as an epic; he introduced characters of a great variety and set about the task of depicting their life in all its authenticity, smiling at its incongruities, admiring its goodness and ridiculing its hypocrisy. He brought to his work mildly ironical tone and imbued it with as solemn a purpose as any epic poet could think of. He knew that he was attempting an entirely new species of literature and was right to claim that 'this kind of writing I do not remember to have seen hitherto attempted in our language'.

Art of Characterisation

Fielding breathed life into the characters he portrayed. Exercising his authority as a comic writer, he avowedly and even ostentatiously refused to go deep into the mind of his characters but this does not imply that he had inferior knowledge of life and people. In fact, Fielding's understanding of people was more intimate than that of most of his contemporaries. Every character of Fielding is capable of having happened whereas, with all its apparent veracity, Richardson's treatment of his characters is at best 'academic'. Fielding astonishes us with authentic, individualised •portrayals of his characters that have been depicted neither as angelic nor as monstrous but as real human beings compounded of both good and evil elements. Fielding studies them with a completely dispassionate observing mind. He gets beneath the external veneer of piety and respectability and gives very realistic portrayals of his characters 'with their lights and shades both in the correct perspective'. On Fielding's art of characterisation, Harold Child, in *The Cambridge History of English Literature* observes:

> Fielding, a master of the philosophical study of character, founded the novel of character, and raised it to a degree of merit which is not likely to be surpassed.

Dialogues

Fielding realises the efficacy of dialogues both in the unfolding of action and the revelation of character and conducts them with exquisite skill. His dialogues are lively as well as natural. Besides, he commands a very wide range. He can be playful and hilarious, solemn and serious, ironical and scathing, sentimental and pathetic, or bitter and pungent as he likes. Richardson had done a good deal for the development of dialogues, but he was greatly handicapped by the epistolary form of narration he employed in all his novels. Fielding however makes a very effective use of them.

Humour

Novel before Fielding was burdened with extra solemnity. Richardson is almost incapable of pure humour; his forte is sentiment. But in the case of Fielding, humour forms a part of his very design of the novel as a comic epic in prose. In his novels, he has employed all types of humour, mainly farcical in *Joseph Andrews,* ironical in *Tom Jones* and satirical in *Jonathan Wild.* Fielding's humour is exuberant, spontaneous, tolerant and exercised on realities. Swift's humour is bitter and springs from his cynicism and his contempt of life in general; Fielding's humour, like that of Shakespeare, derives from a perception of the incongruities in human situation and reveals a great understanding and tolerance on the part of the novelist. Jane Austen, Dickens, Thackeray, the great humourists of English fiction are all indebted to Fielding, the greatest of the great humourists.

Localisation of Scene

Another great contribution of Fielding is the localisation of the scene. In *Tom Jones,* Fielding most carefully considers the problem of geography and in parts works it out. He gives graphic details of Tom's journey to London on the highways. It is true that he describes his settings with broadly conventional strokes and does not feel their significance like Balzac or Henry James, or that he does not care for the natural landscape or the part it can play in human life like Thomas Hardy or D.H. Lawrence; still, in a tentative way, he does indicate the place that nature might occupy in the novel in future.

Englishness of Fielding's Novels

Fielding's novels are thoroughly *English.* Sir Walter Scott says, 'The persons of the story live in England, travel in England, quarrel and fight in England'. Raleigh also observes, 'Fielding's novels are in general thoroughly his own and they are thoroughly English'. Squire Western is a typical eighteenth century Tory country squire. Lady Bellaston too is a contemporary figure. So are Mrs. and Mr. Fitzpatrick, Mrs. Waters, the elder Nightingale, Lord Fellamar, Black George, Thwackum and Square. These characters have typical eighteenth century manners and subscribe to the values of their age. The country squires, the attorneys, the landladies, the gipsies, the highwaymen are all typical products of the eighteenth-century England. The scuffles in the inns, the insecurity of the highways, the duels, the masquerades, the operas are all English. Fielding's frequent allusions to contemporary persons and incidents, though confuse the two planes of actual existence and imaginative creation, reinforce the impression of reality. And yet the characters as well as their experiences have universal validity. Squire Western is a hot-headed despotic father; Squire Allworthy is a generous but gullible landowner; Tom Jones is a generous, chivalrous youth susceptible to women; Blifil is a greedy and malicious hypocrite.

Fielding's Moral Vision

Fielding brought to the novel a healthy moral vision in contrast to Richardson's mawkish, puerile and prudential morality. Richardson measured morality in terms of chastity and treated of chastity as a saleable commodity. With Fielding, morality is an affair of the inner goodness of man. Fielding is tolerant of natural human weaknesses but he does not tolerate hypocrisy. He knows that he who looks pious may be a big scoundrel and he who looks a scoundrel, though not very pious, may yet be a good human being. Hence he urges upon his readers to go beneath the mask and see the reality. Thus Fielding advances a very sound moral philosophy. Coleridge was right in saying that to take up Fielding after Richardson is like emerging from a sick room heated by stoves into an open lawn on a breezy day in May.

Conclusion

So great is Fielding's contribution to the English novel that Walter Scott was tempted to describe Fielding as the father of the English novel. Such a sweeping statement naturally tends to provoke controversy but if we remember that it was not meant as a scientific description and accept only its spirit, it is, to a very great extent, true. Walter Allen sums up Fielding's contribution in the following words:

> The form the novel took in England for more than a hundred years had its origin in Fielding, and in this respect, Smollett, Scott, Dickens, Thackeray and Meredith all wrote in his shadow.

22
Select Literary Criticism

1. F.R. Leavis: A Critical Estimate of Fielding

Fielding made Jane Austen possible by opening the central tradition of English fiction. In fact, to say that the English novel began with him is as reasonable as such propositions ever are. He completed the work begun by *The Tatler* and *The Spectator,* in the pages of which we see the drama turning into the novel—that this development should occur by way of journalism being in the natural course of things. To the art of presenting character and *moeurs* learnt in that school (he himself, before he became a novelist, was both playwright and periodical essayist) he joined a narrative habit the nature of which is sufficiently indicated by his own phrase, "comic epic in prose." That the eighteenth century, which hadn't much lively reading to choose from, but had much leisure, should have found *Tom Jones* exhilarating is not surprising; nor is it that Scott and Coleridge, should have been able to give that work superlative praise. Standards are formed in comparison, and what opportunities had they for that ? But the conventional talk about the "perfect construction" of *Tom Jones* (the late Hugh Walpole brought it out triumphantly and you may hear it in almost any course of lectures on "the English Novel") is absurd. There can't be subtlety of organisation without richer matter to organize, and subtler interests, than Fielding has to offer. He is credited with range and variety and it is true that some episodes take place in the country and some in town, some in the churchyard and some in the inn, some on the highroad and some in the bed-chamber, and so on. But we haven't to read a very large proportion of *Tom Jones* in order to discover the limits of the essential interests it has to offer us. Fielding's attitudes and his concern with human nature are simple, and not such as to produce an effect of anything but monotony (on a mind, that is, demanding more than external action) when exhibited at the length of an "epic in prose" What he *can* do appears to best advantage in *Joseph Andrews. Jonathan Wild,* with its famous irony, seems to me more hobbledehoydom (much as one applauds the determination to explode the gangster-hero), and by *Amelia* Fielding has gone soft.

—from *The Great Tradition* (1948)

2. Martin C. Battestin: Fielding and 'the Great Tradition'; Fielding and Richardson

Tom Jones (1749) is at once the last and the consummate literary achievement of England's Augustan ago. Notwithstanding the whimsy of Dr.

Leavis, who finds life too short for the reading of very many masterpieces, the place Henry Fielding's finest novel holds in 'the great tradition' of English fiction is quite secure. Not just as the mirror of the manners and ethos of an age or as the germi-native influence behind such different writers as Jane Austen and Dickens, Thackeray and George Eliot, Saul Bellow and John Barth but as a work of art in its own right, *Tom Jones* has recently been the subject of more stimulating critical discussion than any other novel of its period.

To be sure, in our century as in his own, Fielding has suffered from the criticisms of those who either have misunderstood his fiction or have found it not very much to their taste. The grounds of Dr. Johnson's preference for Samuel Richardson, "who knew how a watch was made," over Fielding, who could merely "tell the hour by looking on the dial-plate" are not very far from those of Ian Watt's, who distinguishes, to Fielding's disadvantage, between Richardson's technique of "formal realism" and Fielding's "realism of assessment." Between them these two greats novelists, in conscious rivalry, marked out the divergent directions that 'modern fiction was to take— Richardson in *Pamela* (1740) and *Clarissa* (1747-48) turning inward to explore the dark corners of personality. Fielding in *Joseph Andrews* (1742) and *Tom Jones* ranging outward to encompass the variegated panorama of society. In their best and most representative works, *Clarissa* and *Tom Jones,* the differences that separate these authors are absolute, as diametrical as the difference between tragedy and comedy, between the 'realistic' mode and the paradigmatic.

Inevitably, therefore, the claims of Richardson and Fielding for pre-eminence have been debated by readers for more than two centuries. In his own day, the most damaging charge against Fielding was the 'lowness' of his themes—his preoccupation with the adventures (chiefly sexual) of footmen and foundlings, of country wenches and Mayfair demi-reps. Dr. Johnson was appalled that Hannah More had read so 'vicious', so 'corrupt' a book as *Tom Jones,* and a writer in *Old England* fancied that the earthquakes that shook London in 1750 were signs of God's wrath at the enthusiastic reception accorded to Fielding's novel. But the very qualities that offended the prudish and the proper among Fielding's first readers have recommended *Tom Jones* to a twentieth-century audience; Fielding's wit and hearty good humour and, above all, his tolerant humanity have seemed more congenial to us than has the sober—one might almost say pathological—prudentialism of Richardson, however compelling the force of his art in a book like *Clarissa.*

—from *Twentieth Century Interpretations of 'Tom Jones'* (1968)

3. Walter Allen: Fielding's Contribution to the English Novel

The Fielding who wrote novels and the Fielding who put down crime in London can hardly be separated: both activities were expressions of his impulse to reform the manners of the age. Sir Walter Scott called him in the now famous phrase 'the Father of the English Novel'.

The form the novel took in England for more than a hundred years had its origin in Fielding, and in this respect Smollett, Scott, Dickens and Meredith all wrote in his shadow.

—from *Six Great Novelists* (1955)

4. Richard Church: Fielding's Contribution to the English Novel

The importance of Fielding, from an historical point of view, is that he is the first writer to focus the novel in such a way that it brought the whole world as we see it, within the scope of the new rapidly maturing literary form. And those critics who deny that Fielding plunged into the depths, and solitudes of life, where not much of our human experience lies, are deceived by the range and the teeming activity of his work, the speed and pattern of his plot.

—from *The Growth of English Novel*

5. Robert Alter: The Use of Irony in Fielding

On the level of style, irony operates on the reader not only to make him aware of mutually qualifying meanings, but also to implicate him in a particular relationship with the narrator and the material narrated. This relationship is important in winning both his assent to values affirmed through the novel and his sympathy for the kind of literary enterprise that is being undertaken. Irony, as we are often reminded, implies both complicity and superiority—complicity between the ironist and the discerner of the irony, who share a sense, of intelligent superiority to its unwitting objects, or to any hypothetical persons who would take it at face value. The ironic attitude boosts Fielding, and his readers with him, to a firm position of elevation over the world he describes and while few writers since have wanted to rise to such Olympian heights, some of the greatest novelists—Cervantes, Jane Austen, Flaubert, Joyce—have resembled Fielding in maintaining a careful ironic distance between themselves and the life they recorded. The perspective of irony is invaluable because of a danger inherent in the basic impulse of the novel to immerse us in contemporary reality; for reality seen from so close is likely to be a shapeless mass of clamorous particulars which can easily subvert both moral intelligence and aesthetic lucidity. This is clearly one basis for Fielding's objection to the whole method of *Pamela,* for his repeated insistence, contra Richardson, that a novelist must exercise highest degree of selectivity and the finest narrative tact.

—from *Fielding and the Nature of the Novel* (1968)

6. A. R. Humphreys: Fielding's Irony

Fielding's irony illuminates the whole temper of his mind. It has been a commonplace of criticism to dub him a realist, and his subject matter justifies the label; but he shares the real strength of eighteenth-century realism in the imposition on his material of a firm and controlled pattern. The very stiltedness of style in which the more impassioned speeches are written is a mark of this (largely instinctive) formalization. The formal elaboration of speech, though to eighteenth century taste it engaged the reader's emotior more strongly than it can do today, maintained a certain distance an decorum. Tom Jones' addresses to Sophia, for example, are rooted in th good sense which *The Spectator* had made such an integral part of th century's social behaviour. The most familiar difference between Richardsc and Fielding is that the former, by every device in his power, invites the read to indulge in strained and excessively stimulated states of feeling, while th latter, the master of the comic, preserves his own status, and that of the reade as an observer. The rhythmical assurance, the grip over movement, th cogency and unobtrusive symmetry of the sentence, are indices of Fielding real temper, though at present I can only refer to them in passing as the mo potent means of implying the artist's self-control and self-possession.

—from *Fielding's Irony: Its Method and Effects* i
The Review of English Studies, XVIII (194

7. Sir Walter Scott: A general appreciation of 'Tom Jones'

The felicitous contrivance, and happy extrication of the story, whe every incident tells upon, and advances the catastrophe, while, at the san time, it illustrates the characters of those interested in its approach, cannot tc often be mentioned with the highest approbation. The attention of the read is never diverted or puzzled by unnecessary digressions, or recalled to th main story by abrupt and startling recurrences; he glides down the narrati like a boat on the surface of some broad navigable stream, with only win enough to gratify the voyager with the varied beauty of its banks. O exception to this praise, otherwise so well merited, occurs in the story the Old Man of the Hill; an episode, which, in compliance with a custo introduced by Cervantes, and followed by Le Sage, Fielding has thrust in the midst of his narrative, as he had formerly introduced the History Leonara, equally unnecessarily and inartificially, into that *of Joseph Andrew* It has also been wondered, why Fielding should have chosen to leave the sta of illegitimacy on the birth of his hero; and it has been surmised, that he d so, in allusion to his own first wife, who was also a natural child. A bett reason may be discovered in the story itself; for had Miss Bridget be privately married to the father of Tom Jones, there could have been adequate motive assigned for keeping his birth secret from a man reasonable and compassionate as Allworthy.

—from *Prefatory Memoirs to Fielding* (182

8. Martin C. Battestin: Providence and Prudence in 'Tom Jones'

The ideals of good nature and charity, and the tenets of Latitudinari Christianity, may be said to define, in a general way, the ethos of all Fielding fiction. Yet Fielding gave to each of his novels a distinctive character a theme of its own: (he mock heroics of *Joseph Andrews* define the nature Chastity and Charity; the irony of *Jonathan Wild* explores the meaning Greatness; *Amelia* is the rather sentimental story of a marriage. To grasp t distinctive character and purpose of Fielding's masterpiece, we should retu

) the assertion this essay begins with, that *Tom Jones* represents the onsummate literary achievement of England's Augustan age. There are ıany ways of defining Augustanism, all of them perhaps equally true and all qually in need of qualifications. For the present, mine centers upon the orrelative ideas of Art and Order that distinguish much of the thought of the ge of Newton and Pope—an age whose cast of mind saw the moral drama of ıe individual enacted within a frame of cosmic and social order conceived in ne then still compatible terms of Christian Humanism and Newtonian cience, and whose view of art, conditioned by the principles of neo-ristotelian aesthetics, saw the poem as fundamentally mimetic of this niversal design. The philosophic and aesthetic assumptions of the Augustan ge are perhaps most memorably and explicitly expressed in Pope's omplementary poems, the *Essay on Criticism* (1711) and the *Essay on Man* 1733-34), in which the neo-classical concept of Nature and of the poetic mitation of her are set forth in couplets as finely wrought and balanced as the oet's universe itself. The point is most succinctly made in these familiar lines rom the poem that, Fielding once remarked, *"taught me a System of hilosophy* in English *Numbers"*:

> All Nature is but Art, unknown to thee;
> All Chance, Direction, which thou canst not see;
> All Discord, Harmony, not understood;
> All partial evil, universal Good

ope's universe is Fielding's; Art and Order are its distinguishing haracteristics, as they should be of the poem or novel that seeks to imitate 'what really exists" (to cite Fielding's translation of Aristotle in *Tom Jones,* VII.i), and as they will be of the microcosm, man, as long as he realises his rue identity. More than any other production of the age—more even than the *Essay on Man,* which presents a similar doctrine in discursive form—*Tom Jones* embodies this philosophy in a work of the creative imagination.

Art, in this peculiarly Augustan sense, is both the subject and the haracteristic of *Tom Jones.* To promote "the cause of religion and virtue," as Fielding promised in his dedication, the major themes of the novel are the assertion of the doctrine of Providence, or "the Art of God," and the ecommendation of Prudence, or "the Art of Life". Together these two concepts define Fielding's world of Order. As Providence is to the macrocosm, the universe at large, so is Prudence to the microcosm, man—the latter being the rational, pragmatic virtue that, in the moral sphere, is analogous to the Deity's wise and omniscient government of the creation. To a remarkable degree, the art of *Tom Jones* itself is the formal expression of these themes.

—from *Twentieth Century Interpretations of* '*Tom Jones*' (1968)

9. Samuel Richardson: A General Estimate of 'Tom Jones'

.... I must confess, that I have been prejudiced by the opinion of several judicious friends against the truly coarse-titled *Tom Jones;* and so have been discouraged from reading it—I was told, that it was a rambling collection of waking dreams, in which probability was not observed; and that it had a very bad tendency. And I had reason to think that the author intended for his second view (His first, to fill his pocket, by accommodating it to the reigning taste) in writing it, to whiten a vicious character, and to make morality bend to his practices. What reason has he to make his Tom illegitimate, in an age where keeping is becoming a fashion ? Why did he make him a common—what shall I call it ?—and a kept fellow, the lowest of all fellows, yet in love with a Young Creature who was traipsing after him, a fugitive from her father's house ? Why did he draw his heroine so fond, so foolish and so insipid ? Indeed, he has one excuse—he knows not how to draw a delicate woman—he has not been accustomed to such company—and is too prescribing, too impetuous, too immoral, I will venture to say, to take any other bias than that a perverse and crooked Nature has given him; or evil habits, at least, have confirmed in him.

—from a letter to Astraea and Minerva Hill (1749)

10. Samuel Coleridge: The Plot of 'Tom Jones' and Fielding's Morality

What a master of composition Fielding was ! Upon my word, I think the *Oedipus Tyrannus,* the *Alchemist,* and *Tom Jones* the three most perfect plots ever planned. And how charming, how wholesome, Fielding always is ! To take him up after Richardson is like emerging from a sick-room heated by stoves into an open lawn on a breezy day in May.

—from *Table Talk* (1834)

.... I do loathe the cant which can recommend *Pamela* and *Clarissa Harlowe* as strictly moral, though they poison the imagination of the young with continued doses of *tinct, lyttae,* while *Tom Jones* is prohibited as loose. I do not speak of young women; but a young man whose heart or feelings can be injured, or even his passions excited, by aught in this novel, is already thoroughly corrupt. There is a cheerful, sun-shiny, breezy spirit that prevails everywhere, strongly contrasted with the close, hot, day-dreaming continuity of Richardson.

—from *Literary Remains,* ed. H.N. Coleridge (1836)

11. Arnold Kettle: 'Tom Jones' has too much of plot in it; Fielding's attitude to Life

The plot, as numerous critics have pointed out, is worked out with the greatest skill; it is the job, indeed, of the successful professional dramatist Fielding had been. Even more basic to the impression of assuredness is the nature of Fielding's philosophy, skeptical but optimistic. He takes the world in his stride, always curious, frequently indignant, but never incurably hurt. It is not, in the academic sense, a philosophy at all, certainly not a conscious metaphysical system. Rather it is an attitude of mind, an acceptance of certain standards and approaches. Fielding, like most of the writers of the eighteenth century, is very sure of his world. He is not complacent but he is fundamentally confident—confident that the problems of human society, that is to say his society, can and will be solved by humane feeling and right reason. It is this broad and tolerant confidence which gives *Tom Jones* its particular tone and which also (one suspects) alienates those critics who feel less confidence in social man than Fielding, whose optimism they mistake for insensitiveness.

The tentative note can be isolated as emerging from Fielding's constant preoccupation with method. How best to gain the reader's interest ? How to project a character on to the page ? How to achieve any kind of suspense without either playing a trick on the reader or forfeiting his own position as omniscient puppet master ? He is constantly finding that the contrivance of his plot does violence to the characters he has created. The truth is that in *Tom Jones* there is too much plot. Scenes take place which do not arise inevitably from character and motive.

—from *An Introduction to the English Novel* (1951)

12. Walter Allen: Plot construction in 'Tom Jones'

In reading *(Tom Jones),* one is delighted with the swiftness of the narration, the economy, the nimble and inexhaustible invention. Fielding had learnt much from his experience in the theatre, especially how to break up the narrative, set his scene in a minimum of words, and carry on the action in short, swift, passage of dialogue.

—from *The English Novel* (1954)

13. Edwin Muir: Plot construction in 'Tom Jones'

The plot of *Tom Jones* is an adroitly constructed frame work for a picture of life, rather than an unfolding action. The incidents are accurately timed, they come in just where they should suit the scheme of the book; but they are never inevitable, we do not see in them the logic of action,.......

—from *The Structure of the Novel* (1929)

14. E.A. Baker: Plot Construction in 'Tom Jones'

In spirit *Tom Jones* is a close analogue to the grave philosophic comedy of Moliere. It is, however, to a large extent epical in structure or rather an alternation of epical and dramatic, the narrative complicating itself so as to bring various conflicting interests and rival intrigues, to a close encounter, and then, by means of a sudden disclosure, unravelling the complication. In common with epic and with the higher comedy, it is distinguished by the rigorous linkage of cause and effect, the agency of causation residing in the characters, in whom the play of motive is clearly exposed.

—from *The History of the English Novel,* Volume IV (1930)

15. R.S. Crane: The Plot of 'Tom Jones'

It is necessary to look first at its matter and to begin by asking what is the unifying idea by which this is held together. Elementary as the question is, I have not read any answers to it that do not, in one way or another, mistake one of the parts of Fielding's novel for the whole. Doubtless the most common formula is that which locates the essence of the story in the sustained concealment and final disclosure of Tom's parentage. "It is pleasant," writes Oliver Elton, "to consider *Tom Jones* as a puzzle and to see how well the plan works out." For others the most important unifying factor is the love affair of Tom and Sophia; quasi-picaresque sequences of Tom's adventures with women and on the road. The novel, it is true, would be quite different in the total effect if any of these four lines of action had been left out, but it is obvious that no one of them so subsumes all the others as to justifying us in considering it, even on the level of material action, as the principle of the whole. A distinctive whole there is, however, and I venture to say that it consists, not in any mere combination of these parts, but rather in the dynamic system of actions, extending throughout the novel, by which the divergent intentions and beliefs of a large number of persons of different characters and states of knowledge belonging to or somehow related to the neighbouring families of the Allworthys and the Westerns are made to co-operate, with the assistance of Fortune, first to bring Tom into an incomplete and precarious union, founded on an affinity of nature in spite of a disparity of status, with Allworthy and Sophia; then to separate him as completely as possible from them through actions that impel both of them, one after the other, to reverse their opinions of his character; and then, just as he seems about to fulfil the old prophecy that "he was certainly born to be hanged," to restore them unexpectedly to him in a more entire and stable union of both affection and fortune than he has known before.

—from *The Plot of Tom Jones* (1950)

16. Dorothy Van Ghent: Plot Construction in 'Tom Jones'

The plot movement follows the curve characteristic of comedy plots, taking the protagonist from low fortune to high fortune. Tom comes on the scene as a bastard; his very earliest activities enforce the universal opinion .. .that he was certainly born to be hanged; and his reputation and his hope are progressively blackened until he reaches his nadir in London, 'kept' by Lady Bellaston (a circumstance perhaps more reprehensible to a modern reader's eyes than to eighteenth-century's eyes), then accused of murder and thrown in jail, and finally—as if anything still could be added in the way of blackening-presumptively guilty of incest with his mother. But the nadir of his fortune also marks its reversal or crisis, and with the concurrent exposure of Blifil's malicious machinations and of Tom's true goodness, his fortune sails to the zenith of romantic happiness; he proves to be of high birth, he marries the girl of his choice, and he inherits wealth. This is the general plot curve, the concave of comic drama (as against the convex curve taken by tragic drama, a metaphor of plot design that has its origin in the medieval emblem of the wheel of Fortune, on whose spokes people were represented as clinging in various stages of shabby or resplendent clothing, while the wheel turned round, carrying them from doubtful beginning to pleasant endings, or from promising beginnings to unpleasant endings).

—from *The English Novel*: *Form and Function* (1953)

17. Samuel Richardson: 'Tom Jones' is Immoral

Tom Jones is a dissolute book. Its run is over, even with us. Is it true that France had virtue enough to refuse a licence for such a profligate performance ?

—from a letter to J.B. de Freval (1751)

18. Dr. Johnson: Fielding's Superficial Observation and Immorality

Dr. Johnson's comments on Fielding and Richardson have been recorded by his biographer Boswell in his *The Life of Johnson,* Dr. Johnson had a marked dislike for Fielding.

Dr. Johnson believed that Fielding was essentially a 'superficial observer'. He made this distinction between Fielding and Richardson: that Fielding drew only 'characters of manners' while Richardson, being capable of diving into 'the recesses of human heart', portrayed 'characters of nature'. Dr. Johnson maintained that the difference between Richardson and Fielding was the same 'as between a man who knew how a watch was made, and a man who could tell the hour by looking on the dial plate'. Once Dr. Johnson dismissed Fielding's powers of observation with this remark to Mrs. Thrale: "Fielding could describe a horse or an ass, but he never reached to a mule."

—from Boswell's *Life of Johnson* (1772)

Dr. Johnson believed that Fielding's moral outlook was rather undesirable. Hannah More records in her *Memoirs a* remark made by Dr. Johnson when she alluded to *Tom Jones*:

> I am shocked to hear you quote from so vicious a book. I am sorry to hear you have read it: a confession which no modest lady should ever make. I scarcely know a more corrupt work !

—from *Memoirs of Hannah More* (1836)

19. Walter Allen: Fielding's Concept of Morality

Both Fielding and Richardson were moralists and used the novel in order to demonstrate by actual examples what they considered right and wrong behaviour. But their conceptions of morals were poles apart; indeed, each thought the works of the other anything but moral. Certainly the morality of *Pamela* was offensive to Fielding. For Fielding at the heart of right moral lay what he called 'good nature'.

—from *The English Novel* (1954)

20. William Makepeace Thackeray: Fielding's Morality in 'Tom Jones'

Let us, then, not accuse Fielding of immorality, but simply admit that his age was more free-spoken than ours, and accuse it of the fault (such as it is) rather than him. But there is a great deal of good, on the other hand, which is to be found in the writings of this great man, of virtue so wise and practical, that the man of the world cannot read it and imitate it too much. He gives a strong, real picture of human life, and the virtues which he exhibits shine out by their contrasts with the vices which he paints so faithfully, as they never could have done, if the latter had not been depicted as well as the former...Tom Jones sins, and his faults, are described with a curious accuracy, but then follows the repentance which comes out of his very sins, and surely that is moral and touching.

—from a review of Henry Fielding, *Works,* ed. T. Roscoe, *The Times*, 2 September 1840

21. Arnold Kettle: Fielding's Characters Are Flat

And the characters themselves are not, in the fullest sense, people. They are almost all 'flat' characters in the tradition of the comedy of humours, that useful though unsubtle theory based on the crude physiological psychology of the Middle Ages. The very language of the 'humours' tradition lingers on. Tom Jones's 'complexion' is referred to when his amorous exploits are under discussion. Mr. Allworthy's name betrays the manner of his conceptions.

—from *An Introduction to the English Novel* (1951)

22. Dorothy Van Ghent: The Meaning of Human Nature in 'Tom Jones'

But let us step to weigh rather carefully what Fielding means by that 'human nature' which he says is his subject matter, and which we see again and again exposed during that conflict we have described above. Its meaning is not univocal. Broadly it refers to that mixture of animal instinct and human intellection which is assumed to obtain in every personality. But, in many of the incidents in the book, its meaning tips to one side: it tends to lean heavily toward 'animal instinct', simply for the reason that the animal and instinctive part of man is (in the *Tom Jones* world) so frequently disguised or denied by the adoption of some formal appearance. Instinctive drives must therefore be emphasised as an important constituent of 'human nature'. Again, the curious, sometimes beneficial, sometimes damaging uses of intelligence are 'human nature'. We see 'human nature' in the wicked Blifil's calculative shrewdness, in Black George's rationalization for keeping Tom's money, in the absurd intellectual formulas elaborated by Thwackum and Square. But we see it also in Allworthy's high-minded ethics, and in Tom's own idealism. In Blifil himself, 'nature' seems to be congenitally and helplessly bad, and we may be led to speculate on his inheritance from a tenderly hypocritical mother and brutally hypocritical father; and then, in Tom, 'nature' seems to be, on the whole, congenitally good, though he had the same mother as Blifil and a father on whom we cannot speculate at all, as he is not described. Let us sum up these meanings of 'human nature' so far: human nature is a balanced mixture of instinctive drives and feelings and intellectual predilections; it is (dependent on the emphasis given by the specific incident) instinctive feeling alone; it is the human tendency to pervert instinct by intellection; it may be altogether bad (as in Blifil); it may be altogether good (as in Allworthy). Obviously we must expect trickiness in this term, and not be too quick to pin it down to any one meaning. But let us cite another and most important meaning that it has, an ideal meaning which the book strives to give to 'human nature'. Ideally, 'human nature' is what is seen in the best specimens of the human species—a nature to which all should aspire. Under this ideal, it is assumed that the best specimens of the species exhibit a homogeneous configuration of instinct and intelligence—not a suppression of instinct by intellect, nor a suppression of intellect by instinct, but a happy collaboration of the two in the full and integrated man. In this sense, 'human nature' is 'good'. This adjustment Squire Allworthy exhibits from the beginning; but because Fielding has given so many meanings to 'human nature' in his book, we may feel that Allworthy is too crystallized a specimen, not really representative of all the possibilities of 'human nature'; hence the hero, Tom, offers himself more aptly as a representative of 'human nature' inasmuch as he has to learn, with difficulty, the appropriate balance in the process of the action, rather than having it given to him in crystallized form at the beginning. Tom yields formidably and frequently to instinct, and in so doing he exhibits the 'naturalness' and therefore the 'rightness' of instinct as a constituent of the personality, thus correcting the overemphasis on formal appearance which we see in other characters; but at the same time, in these incidents, he shows a remarkable absence of that useful social sense which we call discretion, a lack of which is damaging certainly to himself and a cause of confusion for others. On the other hand, Tom is no fool: he is an admirer of Handel, he philosophizes with dignity in discourse with the Old Man of the Hill—nor could his proposal to Sophia, at the end of the book, be couched in more civilized, more exquisite language. On the whole, 'human nature' in Tom, in all its intricacies and difficulties and mistakes, is a splendid thing; and (and this is its real significance) it is fine and splendid because it is undisguised, it is all out in the sunlight of the social air, the air of common intelligence, readily to be understood, without mask, unpretentious.

—from *The English Novel: Form and Function* (1953)

23. Walter Allen: Why Fielding's Characters Have So Much Vitality

Another source of the vitality of Fielding's characters is the element in which they live, Fielding's mind and style. Like the style of Thackeray, who learnt from him but not enough, Fielding's is that of a man talking to us at his ease. It is direct, unaffected, the product of a mind stored with knowledge of men and of books—he is always driving a point home with an apt quotation, from the classics or from Shakespeare. He is telling a story, the action of which has been long over. Action and characters, therefore exist not only in the context of the story but also in the context of the author's mind, a mind decisive in quality, with firm views on human nature and behaviour. We feel that Fielding knows everything there is to know about his characters even though he does net tell us all. They are so real to him that, even though he may give us no more than a glimpse of them, they become real for us. Behind every simple statement of Fielding's, we feel the force of a deep and varied experience of life, an experience that, however bitter as it may have been, has not darkened the essential humanity of his nature.

—from *The English Novel* (1954)

24. Hamilton Macallister: Minor Characters in 'Tom Jones' Are Types

As for the minor characters, Partridge, Black George, Thwackum and Square, Mrs. Western, the Fitzpatricks, Fellamar—they must be, to a large extent, types. I think with regard to these characters Fielding's general intentions in the novel, his views about human nature—his themes—are all-important. They are full of interest. Partridge is developing continuously as the novel proceeds; his limitations—a tendency to 'blab', physical cowardice, superstition, vindictiveness and uncharitableness—help to bring out Jones's good qualities. Mrs. Western is an example of the new, politically-minded, intellectual woman who one sees often in fiction after Fielding. But I know of no 'Mrs. Westerns' before him; he could have been drawing her straight from life (his novel-writing sister, Sarah Fielding, or Lady Mary Wortley Montague, his cousin ?). But it is essential to the external method that only incidents can show characters, and these people who make short appearances just don't do enough to show more about themselves. Their importance in the novel is nearly always a thematic one. They are there for a purpose: the light they throw on the major characters or on some aspect of human nature.

—from *Fielding* (1967)

25. William Empson: The Character of Tom Jones

Tom Jones is a hero because he is born with good impulses; indeed, as the boy had no friend but the thieving gamekeeper Black George, among the lethal hatreds of Paradise Hall, he emerges as a kind of noble savage. This is first shown when, keen to shoot a bird, he follows it across the boundary and is caught on Squire Western's land; two guns were heard, but he insists he was alone. The keeper had yielded to his request and come too; if Tom says so, the keeper will be sacked, and his wife and children will starve, but Tom as a little gentleman at the great house can only be beaten. "Tom passed a very melancholy night" because he was afraid the beating might make him lose his honour by confessing, says Fielding, who adds that it was as severe as the tortures used in some foreign countries to induce confession. The reader first learns to suspect the wisdom of Allworthy by hearing him say (III.2) that Tom acted here on a mistaken point of honour; though he only says it to defend Tom from further assaults by the bad tutors, who discuss the point with splendid absurdity. Whether it was 'true' one would think, depended on whether the child thought Allworthy himself could be trusted not to behave unjustly. I have no respect for the critics who find the moralising of the book too obvious; the child's honour really is all right after that; he is a fit judge of other ideas of honour elsewhere. Modern readers would perhaps like him better if they realised his basic likeness to Huck Finn; Mark Twain and Fielding were making much the same protest, even to the details about duelling. But Mark Twain somehow could not bear to have Huck grow up, whereas the chief idea about Tom Jones, though for various reasons it has not been recognised, is that he is planned to become awe-strikingly better during his brief experience of the world. You are first meant to realise this is happening halfway through the book, when the Old Man of the Hill is recounting his life and Tom is found smiling quietly himself at a slight error in the ethical position of that mystical recluse (VIII. 13). Old Man is a saint, and Fielding can provide him with some grand devotional prose, but he is too much of a stoic to be a real gospel Christian, which is what Tom is turning into as we watch him.

....

All the actions of Tom Jones are reported to Allworthy and Sophia, and that is why they reinstate him; they are his judges, like the reader. Some readers at the time said it was wilful nastiness of Fielding to make Tom a bastard, instead of discovering a secret marriage at the end, and indeed he does not explain (XVIII. 7) why Tom's mother indignantly refused to marry his father when her brother suggested it. But there is a moral point in leaving him a bastard; he is to inherit Paradise Hall because he is held to deserve it, not because the plot has been dragged round to make him the legal heir.

—from *Tom Jones* in *The Kenyan Review,* XX (1958)

26. William Makepeace Thackeray: Tom Jones does not Deserve to be a Hero

As a picture of manners, the novel of *Tom Jones* is indeed exquisite: as a work of construction, quite a wonder: the by-play of wisdom; the power of observation; the multiplied felicitous turns and thoughts; the varied character of the great comic epic: keep the reader in a perpetual admiration and curiosity. But against Mr. Thomas Jones himself we have a right to put in a protest, and quarrel with the esteem the author evidently has for that character. Charles Lamb says finely of Jones, that a single hearty laugh from him 'clears the air'—but then it is in a certain state of atmosphere. It might clear the air when such personages as Blifil or Lady Bellaston poison it. But I fear very much that (except until the very last scene of the story), when Mr. Jones enters Sophia's drawing room, the pure air there is rather tainted with the young gentleman's tobacco-pipe and punch. I can't say that I think Mr. Jones a virtuous character; I can't say but that I think Fielding's evident liking and admiration for Mr. Jones shows that the great humourist's moral sense was blunted by his life, and that here, in Art and Ethics, there is a great error.

If it is right to have a hero whom we may admire, let us at least take care that he is admirable: if, as is the plan of some authors (a plan decidedly against their interests, be it said), it is propounded that there exists in life no such being, and therefore that in novels, the picture of life, there should appear no character; then Mr. Thomas Jones becomes an admissible person, and we examine his defects and good qualities, as we do those of Parson Thwackum, or Miss Seagrim. But a hero with a flawed reputation; a hero spunging for a guinea; a hero who can't pay his landlady and is obliged to let his honour out to hire, is absurd, and his claim to heroic rank untenable. I protest against Mr. Thomas Jones holding such rank at all. I protest even against his being considered a more than ordinary young fellow, ruddy-cheeked, broad-shouldered, and fond of wine and pleasure.

—from *'Hogarth, Smollett and Fielding'*
English Humourists of the Eighteenth Century, (1853)
a lecture given on 26th June, 1851

27. J. Middleton Murry: Tom's Involvements with Women

It is often forgotten by those who cannot help thinking Tom Jones slightly disreputable that he never lays siege to a woman; it is always the women who beleaguer him. Tom's trouble is that he cannot find it in his heart to repulse them: and this is because he is, fundamentally an idealist about women. Rightly or wrongly, he discerns generosity in the woman's offer of herself to him, to which if he does not respond, he is self-condemned as ungenerous. This does not fit at all with conventional notions of the virtue of chastity, male or female; but it is not incongruous with a delicate and sensitive humanity. Much of Tom's potent charm for us consists in the real, as distinct from and even directly opposed to the conventional, purity he possesses. He is a really innocent soul, where Joseph Andrews is only abstractly innocent; and though he loses some of his boyish naivety, he never loses his innocence. With Molly, he is naive; he entirely fails to see that she is inveigling him. It is not vanity which persuades him he is the responsible party, but his incapacity to conceive that a young woman should be determined to seduce him. And when he has possessed her his reaction is that of a naturally generous soul to generosity. He was, Fielding says, one of those who 'can never receive any kind of satisfaction from another, without loving the creature to whom that satisfaction is owing, and without making its well-being in some sort necessary to their own case.'

—from *In Defence of Fielding* in *Unprofessional Essays* (1956)

28. Michael Irwin: Tom's Four Major Indiscretions and the Part Played by Chance in Their Painful Results

Clearly the reader is meant to see Tom's story, as he himself so specifically does, as a series of follies bringing eventual retribution. Though Tom's misfortunes are not simply the direct consequences of wrong-doing, as for example was Wilson's venereal disease, they do ultimately derive from it.

He commits four major indiscretions, and in each case a chain of unlucky circumstances brings about a painful result.

His affair with Molly Seagrim comes to light purely by chance. Sophia, hearing of the Seagrims' plight from Tom, sends them some money and clothes. The vain Molly wears some of the finery to church, thereby so exciting the jealousy of her acquaintances that a fight ensues in the churchyard. A travelling fiddler, injured in the brawl, applies to Allworthy for a warrant, and in the course of the subsequent inquiry, Molly's pregnancy is disclosed. The outcome of the affair is not very damaging to Tom. Although Sophia resolves to stifle what she now realises to be her love for him, circumstances soon cause her to change her mind. The worst of the repercussions is that Square is able to suggest that Tom's previous kindnesses to the Seagrims have been motivated by lust for Molly, an insinuation which 'stamped on the mind of Allworthy the first bad impression concerning Jones'.

Tom's second indiscretion is his misconduct during Allworthy's illness. Meeting Molly by chance, he is making love with her when surprised by Thwackum and Blifil, and he fights them both off rather than expose the identity of his mistress. The consequences are in this case grave enough. Tom is turned away by Allworthy, thereby being 'separated as closely as possible' from his guardian. Yet these results only ensue through the malice of Blifil, who misrepresents the whole matter, and the ill-luck of the affair's being revealed at a time when Tom is too upset over Sophia to defend himself properly.

Though it is Tom's expulsion from Allworthy's household which physically separates him from Sophia, she herself does not 'reverse her opinion of his character' until learning of his behaviour with Mrs. Waters. Thereupon she leaves Upton without seeing him, convinced that 'he is not only a villain, but a low despicable wretch' (X. 5).

To punish this instance of Tom's folly Fielding has to contrive not only that Sophia shall leave home, but that she shall arrive at the same inn as her lover just after he has succumbed to Mrs. Waters. He has also to arrange that her father shall reach the same hostelry next morning, since it is his intervention which prevents Tom from making an immediate pursuit of Sophia. The morally remedial outcome of Tom's weakness—that he comes later to believe he has committed incest—depends on the large coincidence of his having chanced to rescue the same Jenny Jones who had admitted to being his mother.

Tom's final error, his liaison with Lady Bellaston, depends less on contrivance of plot to produce its unpleasant results. He naturally meets her in the course of seeing Sophia, and it is not unnatural that jealousy should cause her to initiate a plan to punish her lover and her rival. But even here coincidence plays some part in the punishment of Tom. The press-gang sent to capture him happens to arrive at the very moment of his victorious duel with Fitzpatrick, and it is only through the agency of their men that he is arrested and accused of starting the fight.

Fielding makes some effort to place these misdemeanours in an appropriate light, stressing that Tom falls through folly rather than vice.

—from *Henry Fielding*: *The Tentative Realist* (1967)

29. A.E. Dyson: Tom Jones and Squire Allworthy

But why is Mr. Allworthy wrong as often as this ? Is it simply because the plot demands that he should be ? To take this view would be to reduce the novel unthinkably, and fortunately we can discuss it at the start. Mr. Allworthy's failure of judgment is clearly one of the main strands in the moral texture of the whole, and what it indicates is Fielding's profound mistrust of Reason in ethics. It mirrors indeed his unambiguous conviction that a severely rationalistic ethic like Bishop Butler's cannot be relied upon to sift appearance from reality; for even when the gulf between social reputation and true worth is at its widest, unaided Reason may not even be aware that it exists. The one thing Mr. Allworthy lacks is the instinct to smell people's souls. Because he lacks this, all his virtuous striving does not show him where true virtue is to be found.

It is in this, of course, that he contrasts most strikingly with Tom. For Tom has no prudence at all, and his moral judgments are—not in the least conventional, or even rational in their approach. Yet always it seems, he is right about people, and at just those points where Mr. Allworthy is most disastrously wrong. His very vigour and vitality help him to bypass people's professions, their appearances, their reputations and their social facade. He sees straight through to the reality beneath; and if this is partly because his own lack of reputation frees him from convention, it is also because he has moral perceptions of a positive kind which even Mr. Allworthy, for all his goodness, seems to lack. His mercy and compassion are genuine qualities, in the fully Christian sense, whereas Mr. Allworthy's are surrounded with some degree of doubt. Mr. Allworthy always wants to know whether a person deserves mercy; and this is to reject mercy itself in favour of certain notions that are always confused with it—such as the perception of extenuating circumstances, or the generous resolution to give one more chance. Real mercy, like real compassion, is surely undeserved: and both come, in Fielding's presentation of them, from a well of generosity which is very close to the well of vitality and of life itself. In this sense, Tom is actually more virtuous than Mr. Allworthy—though Mr. Allworthy by the nature of things is unable to understand this for himself. Tom's very faults are tinged with the generosity in which his true worth as a person is to be found. This indeed is why Fielding is on his side, and willing to justify him—and not because he is indulgent to Tom's actual faults, as is sometimes supposed.

—from *The Crazy Fabric* (1965) reprinted in
'Henry Fielding: Tom Jones' (Casebook Series) (1970)

30. Hamilton Macallister: Sophia is created in the mould of Shakespearean heroines

Saintsbury classed Fielding with Shakespeare as a writer of comedy, and I think that in Sophia we are reminded often of Shakespearean heroines.......Like Rosalind, from *As You Like It,* and Viola, she combines a fresh simplicity of mind with the courage to go out into the world on her own. She has more physical courage than Viola, who trembled at the idea of a duel. 'A good brisk pace', she says to her maid, Mrs. Honour, 'will preserve us from the cold, and if you cannot defend me from a villain, Honour, I will defend you, for I will take a pistol with me.......' (VII. 7) And when a man rides up to her in the darkness (X. 9) 'she neither screamed out nor fainted away'. Sophia, we see, is generally a more capable character than those other Fielding heroines; she is a Squire's daughter, and an heiress. Like Fanny, she has that simplicity which Fielding associates with the country but it is not a simplicity of mind: '.......her understanding was of the first rate, but she wanted all that useful art which females convert to so many good purposes in life and which, as it rather arises from the heart than from the head, is often the property of the silliest of women' (VII. 3). Much later in terms of experience, when Lord Fellamar calls on her (XV. 2), she is 'somewhat more a mistress of computation'.

—from *Fielding* (1967)

31. Glenn W. Hatfiled: Prudence in Sophia

Always the realist, Fielding is willing to grant that not even Sophia is perfect, for 'we do not pretend to introduce any infallible characters into this history' (III). But in the real world he is trying to describe, the good in any case must acquire some of the craftiness of the bad if they are to survive in that world. The point is, however, that Sophia, in so doing, never really compromises her purity of soul and she is deceitful, unlike Blifil, Mrs. Fitzpatrick, Mrs. Western, Lady Bellaston, *et al.,* only in self-defence. This is the true prudence which Fielding the realist advocates, and the condition of the good person who lacks Sophia's ability to adapt the weapons of deceit to the defence of virtue is suggested to Mrs. Miller: "This poor creature might, indeed, be called simplicity itself. She was one of that order of mortals who are apt to believe everything which is said to them; to whom nature hath neither indulged the offensive nor defensive weapons of deceit, and who are consequently liable to be imposed upon by any one who will only be at the expense of a little falsehood for that purpose' (V). And dramatically this proposition is proved by the ease with which Mrs. Western gets from the well-intentioned Mrs. Miller all of Sophia's secrets.

—from *The Serpent and the Dove*: *Prudence in* '*Tom Jones*'
in *Henry Fielding and the Language of Irony* (1968)

32. Martin Price: Western is perhaps the finest English comic character after Falstaff

In *Tom Jones* the pastoral motive is also present, with the mock pastoral centring in Molly Seagrim and Squire Western. Western is the most startling creation in the novel; perhaps the finest English comic character to have emerged after Falstaff. He is a great baby, frankly selfish and uncontrolled, imperious in his whims, cruelly thoughtless, with the tyranny of a demanding child but none of the capacity to spin out of his appetites subtle schemes of domination or revenge, like Blifil and Lady Bellaston. When he bursts into the London scene, he brings with him the simplicity of the flesh at its most fleshly. He breaks through the code of honour, that most elaborate and attractive of worldly substitutes for goodness, as he breaks through the delicate modesty of Sophia (To her, boy, to her, go to her'). Early in the novel we see his simplicity achieve the same ends as real astuteness. Thwackum and Square compete in praising Blifil, who has maliciously released Sophia's bird; Square sees in him another Brutus, Thwackum an exemplary Christian. 'I don't know what you mean, either of you', Western breaks in, 'by right and wrong. To take away my girl's bird was wrong in my opinion' (IV. 4). And it is he who defends Tom's efforts to recapture the bird for Sophia, 'I am sure I don't understand a word of this', he says to Square and Thwackum, still debating their moral doctrine:

> It may be learning and sense for aught I know; but you shall never persuade me into it. Pox ! you have neither of you mentioned a word of that poor lad who deserves to be commended; to venture breaking his neck to oblige my girl was a generous—spirited action; I have learning enough to see that. D—n me, here's Tom's health ! I shall love the boy for it the longest day I have to live (IV. 4).

It is only to be expected that Squire Western cannot sustain this noble intention. He has as little mind as any man can have; he lives in bursts of enthusiasm, maudlin affection, barbarous willfulness, sheer physicality. He pairs off with his sister—she all Whig politics and would-be townish smartness, he the typical hard-drinking Tory country squire. But Fielding does more with him than that. He uses him to embody animal energy without either the selfish cunning that builds upon appetites in some or the generous charity that fuses with appetite (and transforms it) in others. Tom stands between Western and Allworthy, able to participate in the worlds of both—an innocent carnality in Western and a rational charity in Allworthy—and to bring them together. It would be hard, in fact, to conceive of Tom without the presence of both Allworthy and Western in the novel.

—from 'Fielding: The Comedy of Forms', in *To the Palace of Wisdom: Studies in Order and Energy from Dry den to Blake* (1964)

33. W L. Renwick: Fielding and a Comic Epic in Prose

Taking the phrase as a whole, and allowing that its members, checking and cross-reflecting on one another, do give a notion of the novel as Fielding conceived it, we may yet ask why he troubled with such elaborate allusion to critical theory. The answer is, that Fielding has made a discovery, and an important and delightful one. He had gone out to chase an ass, and found a kingdom. His quick appreciation of the situation is the mark of his greatness, but however delightful the situation, it presented its difficulties. What was this form that was growing under his hand ? It was a literary form, and by all the habits of literature as he had been taught them, it had to be defined. There were no terms *ad hoc,* and in any case the unknown has to be defined in terms of the known. Fielding's kingdom was unexplored and uncharted. If we refer to Aristotle's original triangulation, we find that the non-dramatic equivalent of comedy is lampoon, of tragedy, epic With a new track opening before him and leading across new country, Fielding takes cross-bearings on the old landmarks: and his choice of base-points is as brilliant as it is crucial. *In prose* gives him a third bearing, and his triangulation is complete. He has left the old tracks but he is not lost.

—from 'Comic Epic in Prose' in *Essays and Studies by Members of the English Association,* Vol. 32 (1946)

34. A.R. Humphreys: The Epic Element in 'Tom Jones'

An epic unfolds a large scene and space of time. *Tom Jones* begins before the hero's birth with an agreeable landscape in the manner of Hanoverian topography and with the benevolent Squire Allworthy's house (Gothic as a sign of surviving, or reviving, taste). The foundling hero is discovered, the range of characters expands, through the Allworthy circle, the village folk, the neighbouring Squire Western with his learned lady sister, and (later) his daughter Sophia, and a miscellaneous company of gamekeepers, parsons, inn-keepers and wives, sergeants and soldiers, doctors and lawyers, beaux and libertines, all moving on a well-plotted stage and all tied into the texture of this 'heroic, prosaic poem' by a manner of imagery. Characters have the stored traditional force of standard types, together with a new vitality of fresh observation; Parson Supple is the sycophantic chaplain of Restoration comedy; the doctors Fielding always satirises have their prototypes in Moliere; the learned lady reappears as Mrs. Western: the pedantic or rascally lawyer and justice, the insolent chambermaid or porter, the irascible hunting squire, the hacks of Grub Street—these are part of the traditional portrait gallery. Fielding's hand in them is distinguished for vitality rather than novelty, but the effect of his working with such accepted moulds is to fill the mind with a social pattern that goes beyond the personal and becomes as it were distillation of communal consciousness.

—from *The Review of English Studies,* XVIII (1942)

35. Aurelien Digeon: Comedy in 'Tom Jones'

Fielding's comedy attains in *Tom Jones* its perfect equilibrium. Its most sure characteristic is sanity. More even than that of Moliere, his gaiety leaves an impression of complete satisfaction and well-being. Perhaps the secret of this is the fact that in *Tom Jones* he is careful never to poke fun at one absurdity without also poking fun at its opposite. He jeers at Square but also at Thwackum. If Blifil is odious, Tom Jones is ridiculous. Here, Fielding's laughter is no longer the slave of a formula. His wide and fluid morality allows him to pardon all men, but also, by a natural corollary, commands him to laugh at them all. Neither the perfect Allworthy nor the author himself can always escape a gentle mockery.

The comic element is present in every page. It has settled indeed in the very centre of the work, in the fundamental contrast between the two principal figures, and it is found again, in the tone which the author adopts towards his characters: 'Wait', he says at some point !I am going to introduce my heroines: but you must not think that she is an ordinary woman, etc.' (IV. I). Then this human puppet becomes useless, is thrown aside, and lies as it has fallen, in a droll attitude in the corner of the stage, until the showman's hand needs it once again, picks it up, and once more endows it for an hour or so with life.

There is also comedy in the nice arrangement of events. Providence is frequently kind to the author; and as he admits it himself and is amused by it, we cannot do otherwise than laugh with him. From the general structure of the work it descends to every detail; sometimes, as we have observed, it takes a moral or philosophical direction, but sometimes, and frequently, it is a disinterested comedy. pure laughter, frank delight in incongruous sights. The author himself laughs, he is visibly amused, and little by little we are won by his laughter; by reading of so many joyous adventures which end well we acquire that "gaiety of spirit conceived in scorn of fortuitous event" which is the essential of Pantagruelism.......

Sometimes we get the full-throated laughter of a battle between husband and wife (II. 4) or the amusing homeric struggle so often quoted (at the churchyard, IV. 8).

Elsewhere Fielding seeks a more learned form of comedy. He often obtains amusing results through a surprise or misunderstanding. (For instance, when Sophia and her Aunt Western respectively sing the praises of Jones and of Blifil while each thinks the other is speaking of the same man in (VI. 5). Finally, ore of his most frequent and most personal touches is the sudden contradiction between the deeds and words of one of his characters; philosopher Square, after a high flown discourse, bites his tongue and fails to stifle a course.

—from *The Novels of Fielding* (1924)

36. Ian Watt: Fielding's Personal Intrusion into the Novel

As far as most modern readers are concerned, it is not Fielding's moral but his literary point of view which is open to objection. For his conception of his role is that of a guide who, not content with taking us "behind the scenes of this great theatre of nature," feels that he must explain everything which is to be found there; and such authorial intrusion, of course, tends to diminish the authenticity of his narrative.

Fielding's personal intrusion into *Tom Jones* begins with his dedication to the Honourable George Lyttelton, a dedication, it must be admitted, which goes far to justify Johnson's definition of this form of writing—"a servile address to a patron." There are numerous further references in the body of his work to others among Fielding's patrons, notably Ralph Allen and Lord Chancellor Hardwicke, not to mention other acquaintances whom Fielding wished to compliment, including one of his surgeons, Mr. John Ranby, and various inn-keepers.

The effect of these references is certainly to break the spell of the imaginary world represented in the novel but the main interference with the autonomy of this world comes from Fielding's introductory chapters, containing literary and moral essays, and even more from his frequent discussions and asides to the reader within the narrative itself. There is no doubt that Fielding's practice here leads him in completely the opposite direction from Richardson, and converts the novel into a social and indeed into a sociable literary form. Fielding brings us into a charmed circle composed, not only of the fictional characters, but also of Fielding's friends and of his favourites among the poets and moralists of the past. He is, indeed, almost as attentive to his audience as to his characters, and his narrative, far from being an intimate drama which we peep at through a keyhole, is a series of reminiscences told by a genial raconteur in some wayside inn—the favoured and public locus of his tale.

This approach to the novel is quite consistent with Fielding's major intention—it promotes a distancing effect which prevents us from being so fully immersed in the lives of the characters that we lose our alertness to the larger implications of their actions—implications which Fielding brings out in his capacity of omniscient chorus.......

Few readers would like to be without the prefatory chapters, or Fielding's diverting asides, but they undoubtedly derogate from the reality of the narrative; as Richardson's friend, Thomas Edwards, wrote, "we see every moment" that it is Fielding who "does *personnam gerere,"* whereas Richardson is "the thing itself."

—from *The Rise of the Novel* (1957)

37. Rebecca West: Prefatory Essays in 'Tom Jones'

A few of the essays in *Tom Jones* do deserve cold looks, but in most of them he makes a very fair business of writing an equivalent to Aristotle's *Poetics* for the novel.

—from *The Court and the Castle* (1957)

38. Andrew Wright: The Story of the Man of the Hill

And even within the tale itself are ludicrous extravagances, and at least one classic parallel, or rather backward analogue. Part of the Man of the Hill's tale is *Oedipus Rex* in reverse. Oedipus searches for his father; the Man of the

Hill's father was seeking his son; Oedipus kills a man who turns out to be his father, the Man of the Hill saves the life of a man who turns out to be his father. The alterations are such as to reduce the father-son relationship from the vast and universal to the domestic level. Nonetheless, the adventures of the Man of the Hill have been very far from pretty. His robbery of a friend at Oxford, his cruel and selfish improvident life as a gambler in London, his experience of persons who were cold-hearted, selfish, vain, foolish, and discontented—these experience, together with a self-administered education in the classics and in the reading of the Bible, have made him a misanthrope of Rasselas-like dimension.

—from *Henry Fielding*: *Mask and Feast* (1965)

39. William Empson: The Story of the Man of the Hill

All critics call the recital of Old Man irrelevant, though Saintsbury labours to excuse it; but Fielding meant to give a survey of all human experience (that is what he meant by calling the book an epic) and Old Man provides the extremes of degradation and divine ecstasy which Tom has no time for; as part of the structure of ethical thought he is essential to the book, the key-stone at the middle of the arch. The critics could not have missed understanding this if they hadn't imagined themselves forbidden to have intellectual interests, as Fielding had. For that matter, the whole setting of the book in the 1745. Rebellion gets its point when it interlocks with the theory and practice of Old Man. So far from being 'episodic', the incident is meant to be such an obvious pulling together of the threads that it warns us to keep an eye on the subsequent moral development of Tom.

—from Tom Jones', *Kenyan Review,* Vol. 20 (1958)

40. Hamilton Macallister: Coincidences in 'Tom Jones'

The novel is interlocking pattern of coincidences. Generally it is clear that Fielding planned it, as modern detective stories are planned, to bear this sort of scrutiny. You cheat if you turn to the end. At one point, near the end, he invites us jokingly to believe that Jones will be hanged at Tyburn. We know he won't, but Jones, following the standard pattern of this type of book, blunders from one, apparent, nadir of misfortune to a lower one, becoming more and more hopelessly enmeshed until, suddenly, all is solved. To the reader of 1967, the weakness of *Tom Jones* is quite simply that this is not the pattern of a novel to be taken seriously; it is the 'comic-strip', James Bond pattern. We expect our serious novels, even our serious 'comic' novels, to grow like trees, in which a sort of justice operates throughout—not just at the end. This is the case, broadly, against *Tom Jones.*

—from *Fielding* (1967)

41. William Empson: The Theme of Incest in 'Tom Jones'

My own objection to this bit about incest has long been something quite different, which I should think occurs oftener to a modern reader; and I think the book feels much better when it is cleared up. I thought the author was cheating in a way that whodunit authors often do, that is, he put in a twist to make the end more exciting though the characters would not really have acted so.

—from 'Tom Jones', *Kenyan Review,* Vol. 20, (1958)

42. Robert O. Bowen: The Theme of Incest in 'Tom Jones'

A casual comparison of the morality of *Tom Jones* and the morality of *Hamlet* will show the place Fielding should hold in English literature. In *Tom Jones* the hero believes momentarily that he has committed incest, but when he learns that mechanically he did not, his worry is dropped, which is to indicate that the whole problem of morals to Fielding is one of outer circumstance and not spirit. He is, in fact, a thorough materialist masquerading as a moralist. In *Hamlet* the Prince is driven mad, not by the technical accomplishment of incest but by the idea of it.......The difference between Fielding and Shakespeare in this is the same as the difference between *How to win Friends and Influence People* and the Sermon on the Mount, namely a difference in attitude: huckstering and religion.

—from *Modern Gothic Prose* (1954)

43. Martin C. Battestin: The Allegorical Nature of 'Tom Jones'

In this context the story of Tom Jones's disgrace and redemption, of his arduous journey towards reconciliation with his foster father and marriage with the woman he loves, takes on a broadly allegorical dimension; it is the story of our own deep need to live our lives with Wisdom. *Tom Jones* is not, of course, an allegory in the same sense or in the same way that *The Faerie Queens,* let us say, is an allegory. Fielding's novel differs from the conventional allegory in that its story is primary and autonomous. Characters, events and setting have an integrity of their own and compel our interest in and for themselves; they do not require, at every point in the narrative, to be read off as signs and symbols in some controlling ideational system. Whereas Spenser's Una is "the one," Sophia Western is the girl Tom Jones loves and her family bullies. At the same time, however, within the world of the novel, Sophia is both cynosure and avatar—as her name implies, the centre of the theme of Virtue and its incarnation. In her, to refer again to Fielding's use of the Platonic metaphor in his dedication, Virtue becomes 'an object of sight'. Similarly, though he is not of the same symbolic company as the Red Cross Knight or Bunyan's pilgrim, Tom Jones appears in the novel as a kind of Everyman starving toward maturity against his own weaknesses and the pressures of a hostile world.

Fielding's hero is possessed of every private and social virtue but one: he is honest, brave and generous, but he is imprudent, and therefore imperfect as a moral agent. For want of prudence, Tom Jones is cast out of Paradise Hall, commits one good-natured indiscretion after another, and finds himself at last clapped into prison, rejected by Sophia and his foster father, and guilty (for all he knows) of incest and murder. After his expulsion from Paradise Hall, Tom's journey is at first aimless and uncertain; '*The world,* as Milton phrases it, *lay all before him;* and Jones, no more than Adam had any man to whom he might resort for comfort or assistance' (VII. 2). After the crisis at Upton, however, when his mistress discovers his infidelity with Mrs. Waters, Tom's pursuit of Sophia will signify his gradual and painful attainment of *prudentia.* This we recall, had been Fielding's purpose in writing the novel—to convince men "that their true interest directs them to a pursuit" of Virtue. In prison, at the nadir of his misfortunes, Tom Jones arrives at that crucial moment of self-awareness toward which the novel has been moving: "Sure.......Fortune will never have done with me, till she hath driven me to distraction. But why do I blame Fortune ? I am myself the cause of all my misery. All the dreadful mischiefs which have befallen me, are the consequence only of my own folly and vice" (XVIII. 2). At the moment when Fielding's hero confesses his folly and learns the lesson of prudence, the prison doors miraculously open, his 'crimes' are undone, his enemies exposed, his true identity discovered. His marriage with Sophia follows inevitably. Within the frame of Fielding's comic vision of a just and ordered world, of a world in which Wisdom is attainable, it is the only possible conclusion.

—from *Introduction* to *Twentieth Century Interpretations of 'Tom Jones'* (1968)

44. John Unsworth: The Comedy of Knowledge

Pope's couplet expresses a dilemma that was of particular importance during the Augustan Age—the inadequacy of reason to the discovery of design. Being mortals forced by circumstances to judge and to act, we use inference and interpretation in what we realize is a futile attempt to bridge the gap between our limited perspective and a creator's omniscience.

Fielding's creation is one that relies on its readers for—and to some extent involves them in—its realization. As R.S. Crane noted in 1950, "we may be said to have grasped the plot in the full artistic sense only when we have analyzed [our] interplay of desires and expectations sequentially in relation to the incidents by which it is produced." But Crane himself failed to follow the method he suggested. John Preston, like Crane, argues that Fielding's plot was meant to reflect the chaotic nature of experience rather than universal order. One author's recent assertion, for example, that "if any one learns to judge better, the reader learns" is accompanied by this caveat: "But even that may be too broad a conclusion, for what the reader learns best is caution.......the reader of *Tom Jones* comes to realize that experience resists analysis."

The author's essential power, both to create and to order this chaos, is his control over knowledge. Nothing is more important to the comedy or the drama of *Tom Jones* than the discrepancy between what we know and what the characters know in any given situation, and our awareness of the extent to which a character is ignorant is always a determining factor in how we evaluate his or her action. But what raises *Tom Jones* above the level of simple farce is that it involves the readers as well as the characters in what we may call the comedy of knowledge, and it implicates the reader in the condition of ignorance and partial awareness that it portrays.

—from *Modern Language Quarterly*
(September, 1987)

23
Selected Critical Questions with Answers

Q . 1. "The plot of *Tom Jones*, in its unity and completeness, is nearly as perfect a plot as can be."

"The conventional talk about the perfect construction of *Tom Jones* is absurd."

Adjudicate between these two statements.

The architectonic quality of Fielding's plot construction in *Tom Jones* has elicited applause even from the most fastidious critics of the novel. The most celebrated encomium, of course, comes from Coleridge who considers the plot of *Tom Jones* as one of the three most perfect plots ever planned, the other two being *Oedipus Tyrannus* and *The Alchemist.*

Coleridge's enthusiasm for the plot of *Tom Jones* is not at all unjustified. It is sustained by a single unified idea which according to R.S. Crane (The Plot of *Tom Jones)* consists in initially bringing Tom into an incomplete and precarious union, founded on an affinity of natures in spite of disparity of status, with Allworthy and Sophia, then separating him from both as completely as possible through the villainy of Blifil and the two tutors as well as through his own indiscretions that reverse their opinion of his character and finally, the misunderstandings having been cleared and Tom having matured, in getting him reconciled to the affection both of Squire Allworthy and Sophia. This plot is a single whole and it grows quite organically. Fielding designed it in order to hold the mirror up to nature and the vastness of its canvas tries to incorporate within its frame the variegated eighteenth century life in its different aspects. The action, though topical in appearance, has universal validity. Fielding's chief purpose in presenting this picture of human life was to exhibit the loveliness of virtue and the ugliness of vice, to inculcate the lesson that one's true interest lies in the pursuit of virtue and the avoidance of vice, and to give the warning that virtue needs to be guarded through discretion. Fielding is everywhere in perfect control of his narrative. The episodes are well-knit; the digressions are very few; the harmony between the plot and character is almost perfect and the entire movement of the novel is strictly governed by Fielding's philosophy of life and his moral vision.

Fielding conducts this plot with exquisite symmetry. The eighteen Books of *Tom Jones* can be divided into extremely well-defined three parts, dealing successively with the countryside, the highways and the life in London. The comic peripety at the Upton Inn falls exactly at the centre—Books IX and X. These two Books reintroduce into the action Jenny Jones, the main character responsible both for the initial concealment and the final revelation of the secret of Tom's parentage. Exactly at the centre Tom and Sophia exchange their roles: Tom being followed by Sophia has to pursue her to London after Book X. The two major digressions in the novel, the story of the Man of the Hill in Book VIII and Mrs. Fitzpatrick's account in Book XI are symmetrically interpolated around the centre. Besides, Fielding has used various other devices to achieve structural unity. There are structural similarities: Tom's rural entanglement with Molly is balanced by his urban involvement with Lady Bellaston. The scene in Molly's bedroom is paralleled in the scenes in Tom's bedroom in London. Sophia's first encounter with Blifil is paralleled in Lord Fellamar's interview with Sophia when he tries to rape her. The first scene is repulsive and the second is horrifying so far as Sophia is concerned; but to the readers both the scenes are essentially comic. There are contrasted characters: Tom and Blifil, Squire Allworthy and Squire Western; Sophia and Molly, Sophia and Mrs. Fitzpatrick, Sophia and Lady Bellaston, Thwackum and Square, Tom and Nightingale. The structural unity of the novel is also preserved through the repeated appearance of various objects as well as characters. The hundred-pound bill Sophia had received from her father puts Tom on her track and later it provides him with an excuse to visit her at Lady Bellaston's. Sophia's muff, in the beginning, gives Tom an evidence of her love. At the Upton Inn it reminds him of his sexual laxity and gives Squire Western the impression that Tom is in league with Sophia. Dowling, Jenny Jones, Ensign Northerton, Anderson, are all made to cross Tom's path quite frequently. This, besides knitting the narrative into an organic whole, has the additional advantage of giving significance to details that looked most trivial and characters that looked most irrelevant at their first appearance. In the overall design of the novel, each incident and each character has its own place.

Tom Jones is often criticised for its two major digressions that have already been pointed cut above. But though they do not further the narrative, they are not utterly irrelevant. The old recluse Tom saves from being robbed in Book VIII helps to set off the nobility of Tom. Tom is treated by the world most unjustly but he does not effect a cynical withdrawal from the society like the Man of the Hill. The other digression is even less objectionable. The facts revealed by Mrs. Fitzpatrick do have some bearing on the story since Mrs. Fitzpatrick is an integral part of the action. She on the one hand sets off Sophia's virtue and on the other make, her aware of the dangers of misplaced attachment. And these digressions are quite in accord with the epic conventions too.

In addition, there are a few minor digressions also. Tom's encounter with the gypsies is neither very interesting nor of much service to the plan of the novel. Tom and Partridge's presence at Garrick's performance of *Hamlet* is perhaps intended to be a tribute to the histrionics of the great artist. Fielding also seems to have been swept away by the comic potentialities of the scene and he leisurely dwells upon the comic naivette of Partridge. Although

Fielding does not violate the principles of probability or possibility, some of the coincidences introduced by him come precariously close to the improbable. The sequence of arrivals and departures at the Upton Inn and Squire Western's timely rescue of his daughter almost appear to be contrived. The hurried and huddled ending of the novel gives one a feeling of crowdedness towards the end of the novel. Fielding himself was quite conscious of this, for in Book XVIII, he addresses his reader thus:

> When thou has pursued the many great events which this Book will produce, thou will think the number of pages contained in it scarce sufficient to tell the story.

However, these digressions and other defects of plot construction are too minor to destroy the impression of coherence and symmetry one gets from a close analysis of the novel and almost every reader of Fielding is induced to share Coleridge's enthusiasm for its plot.

Q. 2. Can you justify Coleridge's enthusiasm of *Tom Jones* as one of the three most perfect plots ever planned ?

Or

Comment on the unity and completeness of the plot of *Tom Jones*.

Or

What is meant by the "Architectural qualities" of *Tom Jones* ?

Or

With reference to 'The History of *Tom Jones*' it has been said that "no plot has ever been carried through with more consummate skill."—*(Walter Allen)*. Consider how acceptable this point of view is.

Or

Is there too much of plot in *Tom Jones* ?

For answer, see Q. 1.

Q. 3. Examine the charge of immorality against *Tom Jones* and state whether it can or cannot be sustained.

The charge of immorality against *Tom Jones* was originally stated by Richardson and Dr. Johnson, the avowed Puritan moralists of the eighteenth century. Richardson called *Tom Jones* 'a dissolute book', 'a profligate performance'. Dr. Johnson was even more uncharitable. "I scarcely know a more corrupt book," he wrote to Hannah More. But these views are neither endorsed by posterity nor accord with Fielding's own intention in writing this novel. In his dedication to *Tom Jones,* Fielding makes it eminently clear that he wrote the novel not merely to picture but also to edify. He was sure that his readers would find in the course of the novel 'nothing prejudicial to the cause of religion and virtue, nothing inconsistent with the strictest rules of decency, nor which can offend even the chastest eye in the perusal'.

Richardson takes offence at Tom's being a bastard and the apparent leniency with which Fielding reacts to his sexual aberrations. Perhaps the Puritan in Richardson could not conceive of or tolerate a hero so easily susceptible to feminine coquetry. But Fielding approaches the whole problem from a very different angle. He does not condone Tom's moral lapses. He accepts his vulnerability as a natural human weakness and recommends tolerance while he emphasises the heed of discretion and vigilance to guard one's virtue.

Apart from his love for Sophia which always remains chaste, Tom is sexually involved with three women, Molly, Mrs. Waters, and Lady Bellaston. Taken purely at the superficial level, their evidence is sufficient to condemn him as a depraved wretch who cannot be worthy of Sophia. To see him reconciled to Sophia's affection, in the end is to exonerate his laxity and Fielding should be strongly censured for it. But that is not the whole truth. In order to make a fair assessment of his conduct in these affairs, Tom's involvements call for a much closer scrutinization. The first fact worthy of note is that in all the three cases, Tom is the seduced rather than the seducer. Molly is the senior and the more experienced partner of the two. It is she who is responsible for Tom's practically premature initiation into sex experience. At Upton, Mrs. Waters brings into play all her amorous artillery to overwhelm an adversary who at that moment is interested in nothing but beef and ale. In London, Lady Bellaston exploits his chivalry, his poverty and his love for Sophia for her personal gratification. Fielding tells us that Tom is never less inclined to be amorous than when he meets Lady Bellaston, but he quietly goes on suffering her foul breath, for he knows that it lies only within her power to bring him in touch with Sophia.

Tom's involvement with Molly predates his love for Sophia. He succumbs to Mrs. Waters at a time when there is least hope of his marrying Sophia, for he is not only a penniless bastard but has also lost the protection of Squire Allworthy. In the case of Lady Bellaston he is a victim of ruthless exploitation and deserves sympathy rather than censure. But once he gets entangled in these affairs, he conducts himself very fairly. He is never oblivious of his responsibility towards Molly and courageously confesses his guilt to Squire Allworthy. When Lady Bellaston gets insufferable and Tom grows sick of the insatiable passion of this sex maniac, on the advice of his fellow lodger Nightingale, he proposes to her and manages to secure a temporary release.

Now the circumstances detailed above only extenuate the seriousness of Tom's guilt; they do not absolve him from his responsibility. Nor does Fielding ever forget that Tom has been guilty of these moral lapses and let him escape unscathed. Pursuing our analysis a little further, we find that two of these involvements are highly indiscreet—his drunken rendezvous with Molly in the bushes and his presence in Mrs. Waters's room at the Upton Inn. He is made to pay dearly for both of them. The first one causes his dismissal from the Allworthy estate. The second frustrates his love when it is just on the verge of realisation. The discovery of Sophia's muff in his bed makes Tom remorseful and he realises the importance of continence. His rejection of Arabella Hunt's very attractive proposal to marriage and Mrs. Fitzpatrick's amorous advances which are not different in quality from those of Lady Bellaston offer a clear evidence of his newly developed maturity and emotional stability. He wins Sophia's love only when he comes to deserve it. Does that suggest that Fielding approves of immorality ? And as far as Tom's being a bastard is concerned, Wiliam Empson discovers a moral point even in that: "He is to inherit Paradise Hall because he is held to deserve it, not because the plot has been dragged round to make him the legal heir."

What is the positive concept of morality that Fielding would like his readers to pursue and cultivate. In the dedication to *Tom Jones* referred to above, Fielding declares a threefold intention: to exhibit the loveliness of virtue, to convince men that their interest lies in the pursuit of virtue and the avoidance of vice, and to inculcate the lesson that virtue needs to be guided by discretion. The loveliness of virtue is manifest in characters like Squire Allworthy and Sophia whereas the ugliness of vice is portrayed in characters like Blifil and Lady Bellaiton. Virtue inheres in the inner goodness of heart and a genuine feeling of sympathy for the distress of others. It is here that Fielding deviates from the general puritanic concept of morality advocated by Richardson and company who equate morality with chastity and consider chastity as a saleable commodity capable of securing material prosperity. To Fielding virtue is just the inner goodness of heart and the only certain pleasure it can bring to men is the pleasure of being virtuous that can give immense peace of mind. The greatest vice according to Fielding is hypocrisy that is further analysed as affectation and vanity. Vice is ugly and it brings one internal disquiet and uneasiness. Besides, it is in the nature of vice to bring eventual punishment to those who practise it. Finally Fielding wants to emphasise the need of prudence and circumspection to guard virtue, for virtue can never be safe without them. There is no dearth of women like Molly, Mrs. Waters and Lady Bellaston; all that one can do is to cultivate resistance to their charm.

Fielding is judicious in his approvals as well as censures. He is very ironical when Tom goes into the bushes with Molly, but he appreciates the genuine feeling of happiness that Tom shows at Squire Allworthy's recovery or his genuine concern at Nancy or Mrs. Waters's distress and his overwhelming generosity towards Blifil when he pleads for him to his uncle. He is relentless in his exposure of Thwackum's hypocrisy while he records his satisfaction at Square's last minute repentance He derides Bridget's 'inconsolable' grief at the death of her husband as well as the superior virtue of Blifil when he releases Sophia's bird and appeals to Christian charity in order to hide his jealousy. The temperamental Squire Western cannot rise above the conventional values but he is free from malice or ill will, so Fielding is indulgent with him and regards his violent outbursts with amused understanding and tolerance. But he does not forgive Blifil and he is simply ruthless towards Lady Bellaston. Nightingale, Elder Nightingale, Nancy, Jenny Jones, Partridge, Mrs. Fitzpatrick are all homely, pedestrian men and women, untroubled by ideals but also unstained by villainy. Fielding has deeply studied them, thoroughly understood them and faithfully portrayed their characters. He has left it to his readers to think of them as they like. But his handling of these characters or their circumstances nowhere offends one's moral sensibility. It would be grossly unfair to Fielding to charge him with immorality. In fact, as Lytton remarked, he is a 'deep, accurate and scientific moralist'.

Q. 4. "I scarcely know a more corrupt book than *Tom Jones*"— (Dr. Johnson). Discuss.

Or

"In spite of the adverse criticism of contemporaries like Dr. Johnson, Fielding was as serious a moralist as Richardson himself." Do you agree ? Illustrate your answer.

Or

What is Fielding's philosophy of life as described in *Tom Jones* ?

Or

Fielding, through *Tom Jones* preaches a 'common sense morality' as against a conventional one. Do you agree ?

For answer, see Q. 3.

Q. 5. Show that *Tom Jones* vividly reflects the contemporary English life.

Once William Hazlitt declared, and quite justifiably too, that Fielding's novels throw more light on eighteenth century society of England than the whole mass of statistical and historical documents. Indeed the entire life in its panoramic expanse, taking in its sweep the countryside, the highways and the urban society of London is marvellously recreated in his epical work *Tom Jones*. In this respect Fielding's work marks a definite advance over the literary writings of his predecessors who portray the social life but meagrely and in parts only. Even Fielding, as a rule, eschews elaborate details of external appearance, yet by graphic and suggestive touches he provides a remarkably distinct and vivid impression of the externalities of his age.

Country Life

Though the countryside is more conducive to the cultivation and preservation of virtue yet Fielding does not present it as a pastoral idyll. It is a narrow world allowing to its inhabitants an intimate familiarity capable of breeding vicious gossip. Here we meet the prude in Mrs. Deborah Wilkins, the shrew in Mrs. Partridge, the champion of women's lib in Mrs. Western, the amazon in Goody Brown, the coquet in Molly Seagrim. The male world with the two young lads Tom and Blifil, the two Squires Allworthy and

Western, the two tutors Square and Thwackum, and Partridge and Black George to add spice to it, offers a colourful spectacle. The wealth and splendour of the English countryside—Tom eats three pounds of roast beef at a sitting and Squire Western and Parson Supple share four bottles of wine—is set beside the poverty and squalor of the Seagrims' life. There is a good deal of vanity and affectation, malice and intrigue, destroying its peace. Yet in contrast with London, it definitely presents better soil for virtue to flourish in.

The Highways

The six Books in the middle of the novel describe Ton's adventures on the highways leading to London. These highways were infested with robbers and villains. It was very difficult for young women to travel along these lonely roads in the night. Tom rescues Mrs. Waters from Ensign Northerton and the owner of the puppet show attempts an assault on Sophia's virtue. Two bandits try to rob the Man of the Hill of his belongings and a highwayman threatens Tom at the point of his pistol to hand over to him all his valuables. The inns on the way harbour many rowdy and undesirable elements and present quite a noisy scene. Fielding has, indeed, given a very authentic description of the wretched condition of the eighteenth century highways.

Life in London

In the story of the Man of the Hill, we get a premonition of the life in London much before Tom enters that great city. The London society is morally degenerated. Lady Bellaston is a debauch; Lord Fellamar is a cowardly rascal; Nightingale, though not wicked basically, is a moral coward; the elder Nightingale has an eye only for material advancement. This is a world of duels. Squire Western is challenged by Lord Fellamar's messenger and Tom has a duel with Mr. Fitzpatrick. And people can be easily bought to give false evidence even though it might imperil the very life of a person. The apparent elegance and refinement of the aristocratic society is merely an affectation. Fielding also tells us that despite the plays and the masquerades, the high life is rather dull and affords very little humour or entertainment. In one of the prefatory chapters, he says:

> ....here except among the few who are engaged in the pursuit of ambition, and the fewer still who have a relish of pleasure, all is vanity and servile imitation. Dressing and cards, eating and drinking, bowing and courtseying make up the business of their lives

However, Fielding believes that these people are more frivolous than licentious.

Public Schools, Medical Profession, Law

Public school education seems to be unsatisfactory, for Squire Allworthy, believing that Tom and Blifil would be unavoidably exposed to corrupting influences in a public school, decides to engage private tutors for the children.

Doctors had very inadequate professional knowledge. Fielding gives a very humorous picture of doctors:

> To say the truth, every physician almost hath his favourite disease, to which he ascribes all the victories obtained over human nature The gout, the rheumatism, the stone, gravel, and the consumption, have all their several patrons in the Faculty; and none more than the nervous fever, or the fever on the spirits ....

But Fielding having been a magistrate himself, it is the defective legal system that has been exposed most ruthlessly. Fielding observes most painfully that most of the judges behaved as if they were a law unto themselves and gave a very partial judgment. They often exceeded their authority. Squire Western once wanted to commit a maid to Bridewell, the Correction House, merely for insolence. Squire Allworthy had almost decided to send Molly to the jail though no regular and decisive evidence had been laid against her. Judges used to commit acts of injustice and felony by cognising insufficient or false evidence. In the case of game laws, the judges made a very arbitrary use of their discretion. Again, Squire Western strictly enforced the law against swearing while he quite conveniently forgot that he himself was addicted to swearing most loudly. Fielding also gives a fine parody of the legal jargon when Tom is subjected to an improvised sort of trial at Upton for abducting Sophia and stealing her muff. However, it should not be concluded that all judges were corrupt or rash in their judgment, for Squire Allworthy at least patiently heard all evidence available and took pains to arrive at the correct decision.

Women

A very ugly aspect of the status of the English women is mentioned in the novel. Loss of chastity was considered to be a very heinous crime and a woman who had lost her chastity was branded as a fallen woman acceptable to none. Even the person who was responsible for her degradation did not consider it respectable to marry her. Thus Nightingale, though himself responsible for Nancy's pregnancy and not totally disinclined to marry her, found it humiliating to accept her. And Lord Fellamar was persuaded into the belief that it would be easy for him to marry Sophia after having raped her. This is precisely Clarissa's predicament in *Clarissa.* However a movement to secure for women a status equal to that of men had already started. At one stage, Mrs. Western tells her brother:

> How often have I told that English women are not to be treated like Ciracess slaves. We have the protection of the world: we are to be won by gentle means only, and to be hectored and bullied and beat into compliance.

At another moment she says, "Woman in this land of liberty cannot be married by actual brutal force."

Political Situation

Political situation of the contemporary England is also reflected in the novel. In 1745, the 'Bonny Prince Charlie' made an attempt to assert his claim to the English throne in order to reinstate the Stuarts. An army was sent northwards to combat the rebels. It is to the soldiers of this army that Tom gets attached in Book VII. In Book XI, while Sophia and Harriet are staying at an inn, Sophia is mistaken for Prince Charlie's mistress Jenny Cameron and the landlord feels that most probably these ladies have taken a roundabout path to London in order to escape the Duke of Cumberland's army.

Conclusion

Thus we observe that practically all aspects of English life are portrayed in *Tom Jones* with a degree of authenticity rarely surpassed in the entire range of English fiction. *Tom Jones* is not just the history of Tom Jones, the foundling: it is the social history of a nation. Fielding's greatness lies in the fact that he does not let his work degenerate to the level of a period piece as usually happens in a novel or a play of manners. He gives his action universal validity making *Tom Jones* an epic not merely of England but of whole mankind.

Q. 6. What value, if any, has *Tom Jones* as a social document ?

Or

***Tom Jones* is to be valued as a panoramic commentary on mid-eighteenth century England and not as a serious study of human nature." Discuss.**

Or

"In *Tom Jones* the eighteenth century is embodied, not entombed." Discuss.

Or

"Fielding has the undeniable merit of representing certain aspects of contemporary society with a force and accuracy not ever rivalled by any other writer." Discuss this statement with special reference to *Tom Jones*.

For answer, see Q. 5.

Q. 7. "Tom Jones was a new type of hero, one might say, the unheroic hero." Sketch the character of Tom Jones in the light of this remark.

When we first meet Tom Jones, he is a foundling mysteriously discovered in Squire Allworthy's bed. Mrs. Deborah Wilkins, assuming that he is a bastard, comments:

> It goes against me to touch these misbegotten wretches, whom I don't look upon as my fellow creatures. Faugh ! how it stinks ! It doth not smell like a Christian.

We realise at this very moment that Fielding intends introducing an entirely new kind of a hero, the unheroic hero, and indeed as he grows up, he confirms, by his well-intentioned but imprudent and indiscreet actions, that he was 'born to be hanged'. The apparently sober, discreet and pious nature of Blifil tends to confirm this opinion.

In Tom Jones, Fielding has depicted the character of an ordinary, noble but weak man. His impulses are good but unrestrained. He is honest, brave and generous but extremely weak-willed. The first few episode; dealing with poaching, his persistent lying to save Black George from getting a sack, his selling his horse as well as the Bible to save the gamekeeper's family from starving, his rescuing Sophia even at the risk of his own life reveal his courage and his inherent goodness of heart. But his major weakness is his easy susceptibility to feminine charm; he is *l' homme moyen sensuel.* His first love is Molly Seagrim, the gamekeeper's daughter. He is just swept off his feet by her beauty and is easily seduced by her, since she is the more experienced partner of the two. Later, he gradually develops a passion for Sophia, which puts him in a great moral dilemma. In all fairness to Molly, he does try to resist Sophia's charm though finds the resistance very hard. This love triangle betrays his moral levity. True, it is Molly's infidelity, exposed through the discovery of the philosopher Square in her room and her sister's evidence that the child she is carrying was most probably fathered by Will Barnes that makes Tom feel absolved from all responsibility towards her; it cannot, yet, be denied that Tom had originally gone to Molly's room to offer her financial help in order to secure freedom to woo Sophia. Fielding has, with great veracity indeed, portrayed Tom's fallibility. By nature, he is sanguine and boisterous. His animal instincts dominate; and he neither knows how to discipline them nor realises the importance of any such discipline. If he has to celebrate his benefactor's recovery, all that he can do is to get drunk. Then he falls into a reverie to meditate on Sophia and to let his lively imagination paint her in various ravishing forms. He declares that Sophia, and Sophia alone, could make him happy and takes out a pen-knife to engrave her name on every tree. But just then there appears Molly, coarsely dressed, smelling of sweat as a result of day's labour, with a pitchfork in her hand, and after a brief parley, they retire into the thickest part of the grove. What is deflation ! Which conventional hero would degrade himself to this !

At Upton, Tom is oblivious of Mrs. Waters's charms only as long as he is hungry. But once he has taken his fill, he at once succumbs to her 'artillery of love' and allows his fair conqueror to enjoy the fruit of her victory. In London he allows himself to be seduced by Lady Bellaston, a middle-aged, wealthy, corrupt woman of society, and, what arouses the indignation of many of the readers, even accepts money from her. Now, Fielding does not approve of Tom's sexual irregularities. Basically they expose his weakness. But Fielding wants to suggest that this weakness is a general human weakness and is shared by most of the people. Tom Jones is weak-willed and imprudent but neither irresponsible nor ungenerous and has both the insight to recognise his mistakes and the honesty to own them and repent for them. This is what redeems him. The episode at the Upton Inn strengthens his resolve to be disciplined and it is because it lies only within Lady Bellaston's powers to put him in touch with Sophia that he allows himself to be sexually exploited. It might be a perverted logic that inhibits him to get encashed Sophia's hundred-pound bill but recommends acceptance of money from Lady Bellaston, but logic it is. And whatever money he accepts from her, he immediately offers to Mrs. Miller to relieve the distressed family of the Andersons. What a mixture of indiscretion and nobility and how unlike a conventional romantic hero !

Tom *Jones* is Tom's journey towards self-realisation. At Upton, so near fulfilment, and yet frustrated through his own laxity, he violently curse both Partridge and Mrs. Waters, but most of all himself. His mad outrage is also a sign of awakening. In London, he resists the amorous advances of Mrs. Fitzpatrick and rejects a very attractive proposal of marriage from Mrs. Arabella Hunt. He admits that it is not Blifil who has caused his downfall but his own conduct and in a very touching letter to Sophia, he confesses his unworthiness along with bitter lamentation of despair and solemn protestations of unalterable fidelity to her. In Book XVIII, chapter 2, when he is in prison, he arrives at a moment of self-awarenes:

> Sure.......Fortune will never have done with me till she hath driven me to distraction. But why do I blame Fortune ? I am myself the cause of all my misery. All the dreadful mischiefs which have befallen me are the consequences only of my own folly and vice.

In Book XVIII, chapter 10, on his reconciliation to Squire Allworthy, he says,

> ....my punishment hath not been thrown away upon me: though I have been a great, I am not a hardened sinner; I thank Heaven, I have had time to reflect on my past life, where, though I cannot charge myself with gross villainy, yet I can discern follies and vices more than enough to repent and to be ashamed of; follies which have been attended with dreadful consequences to myself, and have brought me to the brink of destruction.

And in Book XVIII, chapter 12, he entreats Sophia:

> Alas ! madam, it is mercy and not justice, which I implore at your hands. Justice, 1 know must condemn me.......

But though Tom insists that he is an irredeemable fool, in fact, as Sophia herself vouchsafes, he is possessed of great goodness of heart. He not only does not hurt anyone consciously but also goes even out of the way to help others. He enrisks his own life to retrieve Sophia's bird, to rescue the Man of the Hill from ruffians or Mrs. Waters from Ensign Northerton. He overpowers the highwayman, but on learning his distress, offers him whatever little he can. Black George gets his forgiveness and so does Blifil, though responsible for most of his miseries. Squire Allworthy is prompted to comment, "Child, you carry this forgiving temper too far."

Since Tom had every private and social virtue except prudence, it is prudence that Squire Allworthy tries to teach him in Book XVIII, chapter 10:

> Prudence is indeed the duty which we owe to ourselves; and if we will be so much our own enemies as to neglect it, we are not: to wonder if the world is deficient in discharging their duty to us; for when a man lays the foundation of his own ruin, others will, I am afraid, be too apt to build upon it.

But Tom had already been learning to be prudent and repenting for his past follies. His repentance on the previous occasions had proved temporary for he was yet emotionally immature, but now, after 'all his sufferings, he has developed enough emotion stability to assure us of constant discreet conduct.

Tom Jones, we thus observe, is quite unlike the old heroes of the French romances, embodiment of all virtues, infallible and incorruptible. He is an ordinary human being, aware of his weaknesses, striving hard to work out his redemption and eventually achieving it. Walter Allen is right to remark that "Tom Jones was a new type of hero, one might say the unheroic hero."

Q. 8. Dr. Johnson agreed with Richardson in thinking that the 'virtues of Fielding's heroes were the vices of a truly good man'. What is your opinion ? Justify your answer.

For answer, see Q. 7.

Q. 9. Show that *Tom Jones* belongs to that class of novels, the aim of which is to present, by a multitude of characters, a complete picture of human life.

In *Tom Jones,* Fielding has given us an enormous gallery of characters—there are more than forty of them, fully developed, marvellously differentiated. These characters have been taken from various fields of life and they include among them the country squires, the philosophers, the clergymen, the doctors, the lawyers, the highwaymen, the innkeepers, the gamekeepers, the soldiers, the gypsies, the aristocrats. They are embodiments of a multitude of human qualities—generosity, magnanimity, chivalry, hypocrisy, pretence, malice, avarice, vanity, coquetry, timidity, etc. Fielding has not created these characters merely for the sake of creating characters. He has populated his world, taking within its folds the countryside, the highways and the urban society of London, with this host of diverse figures, representative of such variety of dominating characteristics, in order to present a faithful picture of human nature as a whole, and it cannot be denied that he has eminently succeeded in his purpose.

Tom Jones is divided into three parts consisting of six Books each. The first six Books deal with the countryside where, through the depiction of happenings mainly on two neighbouring estates, Fielding has been successful in highlighting the major aspects of a homely, pedestrian sort of life. Incidents look quite trivial—a bastard given protection by a kind squire, an illegitimate birth imputed to a poor woman, a marriage of convenience of an ageing spinster to an opportunist captain, betrayal by an ungrateful brother, a skirmish in a family, a brawl at a church, the growing passion of an adolescent lad for an adolescent girl, rivalry of two lads, a few good-intentioned, a few inadvertent indiscretions, misunderstandings and injustices—this is what transpires on the estates of Squire Allworthy and Squire Western. These characters are endowed with remarkable vitality and their mutual involvements help in projecting a very faithful, interesting and satisfying picture of the country life on the whole.

The next six Books take the narrative meandering along the highways to London. It is a strange world indeed, this world of innkeepers, stage coaches, soldiers, gypsies, gangsters and highwaymen. Here, Fielding is able to have a close look at the castaways of the society. Tom, first of all, is provided with his Sancho Panza, the school master-turned-barber-surgeon, the artless prattler Partridge. Here we meet the respectable-looking Ensign Northerton who can stoop so low as to attempt strangulation, for some very petty belongings, on a woman who is willing to elope with him for love or lust, whatever it be. Here we meet the saintly-looking old recluse who is in fact a cowardly cynic. Then there is a highwayman who is, in reality, a poor honest man, driven to such ignoble means by the distress of his starving family. There are also the gypsies with their strange moral ethics that decree punishment to the husband of the woman caught for adultery and not the man who is her partner in the crime. The adventures contrived by Fielding faithfully recreate life along the eighteenth century English highways, but there is nothing topical or ephemeral about the human experience depicted in them, which retains its universal validity throughout.

The urban society of London offers, quite naturally, a much greater variety. It is a world of plays, operas and masquerades, but it is also a world of betrayals and desertions, duels and intrigues, that one could not even dream of in the countryside. An aristocrat can attempt a rape on a young, chaste virgin to force her into marriage and can remain completely untroubled by any moral scruples. A middle-aged, depraved woman of society can plot the impressment of a youngman simply because he is no longer prepared to gratify her insatiable sexual demands, can feel happier to see him convicted of murder and thinks nothing of it. An avaricious father is willing to force his son into an insufferable marriage alliance and cause the utter ruination of the girl he loves simply because the match intended by him can bring a little extra money. It is a disgusting world indeed but Fielding makes no attempt to make it less odious. Tom's ingenuity and nobility looks dazzling in this dark realm of sinister motives and diabolical actions.

This appears to be a panoramic view of human society. However, there are, also, a few limitations to it. The aristocracy, in spite of Lady Bellaston and Lord Fellamar, is not adequately and convincingly represented. This exclusion appears to be deliberate. The nobility, in Fielding's age, was leading a highly sophisticated but artificial life. Its distinctive features were obscured by a dull uniformity of good manners. As such it offered very little scope to a delineator of human nature like Fielding. He felt more interested in the middle and lower classes which 'expressed their thoughts and feelings with more artless frankness, and took less trouble to hide their personal peculiarities under the cloak of formal propriety.

Secondly, Fielding felt more interested in the 'ordinary human nature, not exceptionally glorified, not exceptionally debased'. He had little experience of heights and depths in human nature. 'He could not understand either a great saint or a great sinner. He had no comprehension of spiritual fervour or exaltation, which he would have deemed a mere ebullition of hypocrisy or folly; nor, on the other hand, did he really plumb the abysses of the reprobate and abandoned soul'. That is why he could not portray convincingly an irredeemed villain like Blifil. Blifil's villainy, manifest in his ulterior designs is of the same class as that of Iago, but Blifil is less alive and less plausible than Iago. The same, to a lesser extent can be said, of Allworthy, Fielding's concept of an altogether good man. But these shortcomings apart, *Tom Jones* does attempt almost a complete picture of human life.

Q. 10. "Fielding's attitudes, and his concern with human nature, are simple, and not such as to produce an effect of anything but monotony." Consider with reference to *Tom Jones*.

Prof. Martin C. Battestin, the editor of the *Twentieth Century Interpretations of "Tom Jones'* gives this title to the excerpts he has included in his collection from Dr. F.R. Leavis's work: *"Tom Jones' and the Great Tradition: A Negative View.* Really Dr. Leavis, utterly unimpressed by the unqualified praise lavished on Fielding during the past two centuries fails to appreciate Fielding's genius and expresses an unabashedly negative view of *Tom Jones* He records his disgust of the conventional talk about the perfect construction of *Tom Jones* and does not agree that Fielding commands any wide range and variety in it. Towards the end, Dr. Leavis makes this comment:

> Fielding's attitudes, and his concern with human nature, are simple, and not such as to produce an effect of anything but monotony (on a mind, that is, demanding more than external action) when exhibited at the length of an "epic in prose".

Frankly, it is not 'objective or disinterested criticism'. Dr. Leavis is known for. His stigmatising remarks proceed from his prejudices and must be dismissed as most uncharitable. It is not just the architectonic exquisiteness of *Tom Jones* that elicits applause, though it alone could place Fielding very high among the English novelists; it is the fact that Fielding's characters are nowhere subordinated to requirements of any formula that may be governing the plot. These characters follow their own instincts and inclinations and yet the plot trace, such a neat and elegant pattern. Where else could one come across such 'happy contrivance' ? And it is deliberate ignoring of obvious facts to say that Fielding's range is narrow or limited.

Dr. Leavis believes that Fielding's attitude towards human nature is simple. He is prompted to make this comment because action in *Tom Jones* is externalised. But it is not at all essential that an externalised action traces only a simple pattern and betrays the lack of perceptivity or incapability of expression in an author, while a concern with the inner conflicts also successfully reveals the intricacies of the inner mind. *Tom Jones,* in its broad outlines, assumes something of an allegorical dimension. It is the story of everymans recognition of his folly and fallibility and his persistent endeavour towards self-realisation and redemption. Action on such a universalised level is bound to be simple but symbolic. Besides, there are many other reasons, enlisted by Ian Watt in his book *The Rise of the Novel,* for Fielding's predominantly external approach to characters. Though Richardson tried to peep into the dark labyrinths of human mind, and was praised for it, the eighteenth century public, with its preoccupation with reason and good sense, considered it breach of decorum. Lady Mary Wortley Montagu pointed out, it was very bad manners for Richardson's heroines to 'declare all they^ think since 'fig leaves are as necessary for our minds as our bodies. The avoidance of intimate and confessional approach to personality was also consistent with the classical tradition as a whole. But above everything else, Fielding's comic purpose itself required an external approach. 'If we identify ourselves with the characters , writes Ian Watt, 'we shall not be in any mood to appreciate the humour of the larger comedy in which they are visible participants'.

What Fielding loses through the depiction of externalised action, he makes up through its variety. Fielding declares that his subject matter in the novel is human nature, which implies a balance, in a certain proportion, of instinctive drives and feelings and intellectual predilections. The proportion determines the stamp of the personality and produces some very interesting specimens: the good-intentioned but morally blind and gullible Squire Allworthy, the hot-headed, hard-drinking, hard-swearing but affectionate and indulgent Squire Western, the generous but weak-willed Tom, the scheming villain Blifil, his ungrateful father Captain Blifil, the beautiful and magnanimous Sophia, the hypocritical philosopher Square and divine Thwackum, the naive babbler Partridge and his shrewish and domineering wife Mrs. Partridge, the self-opinionated Mrs. Western, the coquettish Molly Seagrim, the generous but sexually lax Jenny Jones, the debauched and depraved Lady Bellaston, the sophisticated but foolish Lord Fellamar, the rakish Mr. Fitzpatrick, the simple and easily deceivable Mrs. Miller, the timid Nightingale and his prudential father the Elder Nightingale—couldn't one marvel at such a prodigious variety of characters ? And when they are made to act and react to one another in the dramatic manner revealed by the novel, in that inimitable style of Fielding, can it be justified to say that the effect produced is that of monotony ?

In *Unprofessional Essays,* John Middleton Murry attempts a bold defence of Fielding. 'Because Dr. Leavis has savoured the very different satisfactions that Jane Austen, George Eliot, Henry James and Joseph Conrad have to offer', asks Mr. Murry, 'has he become incapable of taking delight in Fielding's novels ?' In his own delightfully ironical tone, Mr. Murry also tries to discover why Dr. Leavis, who admires Jane Austen and George Eliot and also appreciates George Eliot's profound admiration of Jane Austen, fails to admire Fielding or take a note of George Eliot's profound admiration of Fielding. Mr. Murry writes,

> I humbly suggest it is because Fielding's novels do not lend themselves to the kind of treatment which Dr. Leavis delights to exercise upon the novel. They being devilishly little grist to his highly specialised mental processes. The moral preoccupations with which they are concerned—and really, in spite of Dr. Leavis's pronunciamento, they have each a moral preoccupation—are not of the sort that makes an impression upon him. Their durable achievement, in the creation of characters of whose reality we are convinced and who abide in the memory, is one which he cannot recognise because he cannot account for it by his critical methods.

We may conclude that neither Fielding's attitudes towards human life are simple nor his concern with human nature is superficial. He has a more intimate knowledge of life and manners than either Defoe or Richardson, the other eighteenth century novelists; his perception is clearer and keener; his depiction is more authentic and more convincing; his style, gay and ironical, is more fascinating and just carries the readers away in its sweep. It might appear presumptuous to differ with as great a critic as Dr. Leavis, but I believe, it is presumptuous even of Dr. Leavis to imply, as he does in his essay, that it is reasonable and right for him to be bored by Fielding because he is a person with a mature mind, and a mature mind must, of necessity, be bored by Fielding.

Q. 11. "Fielding avowedly and even ostentatiously refused to go deep into the minds of his characters." Expand this into an essay on Fielding's characterisation.

In *Joseph Andrews* Book III, chapter 1, Fielding says that in writing his novels, his purpose is to show 'not men, but manners; not an individual, but a species'. Dr. Johnson also made a distinction between Richardson and Fielding by saying that Richardson drew characters of nature while Fielding drew characters of manners. It is, indeed, true that Fielding does not try to individualise his characters by analysing their innermost, conflicts the way

Richardson does. Ian Watt, in his book *The Rise of the English Novel,* comments:

> At all events Fielding avowedly and even ostentatiously refused to go too deep into the minds of his characters, on the general grounds that "it is our province to relate facts and we shall leave causes to persons of much higher genius."

In Book III, chapter 4, Fielding refuses to analyse Blifil's feelings saying that 'it would be an ill office in us to pay a visit to the inmost recesses of his mind, as some scandalous people search into the most secret affairs of their friends, and often pry into their closets and cupboards, only to discover their poverty and meanness to the world.' Similarly in Book IV, chapter 3, when Fielding comes to present Sophia's feelings when she first learns of Tom's love, he excuses himself in the words: 'as to the present situation of her mind I shall adhere to the rule of Horace, by not attempting to describe it from despair of success'.

Ian Watt tells us that Fielding was not 'interested in the exact configuration of motives in any particular person's mind at any particular time but only in those features of the individual which are necessary to assign him to his moral and social species. He therefore, studies each character in the light of his general knowledge of human behaviour, of 'manner', and anything purely individual is of no taxonomic value. Nor is there any need to look inside; it, as Johnson said, Fielding gives us the husk it is because the surface alone is usually quite sufficient to identify the specimen—the expert does not need to essay the kernal.' He also enlists three other reasons for Fielding's predominantly external approach to characters 'To begin with, the opposite approach involved a breach of—decorum as Fielding's cousin Lady Mary Wortley Montagu pointed out it was very bad manners for Richardson's heroines to declare all they think', since 'fig leaves are as necessary for our minds as our bodies' It was also consistent with the classical tradition as a whole., to avoid the intimate and confessional approach to personality...Lastly, Fielding's comic purpose itself required an external approach, and for a compelling reason. If we identify ourselves with the characters, we shall not be in any mood to appreciate the humour of the larger comedy in which they are visible participants: life we have been told, is a comedy only to the man who thinks and the comic author must not make us feel every stroke of the lash as his characters squirm under his corrective rod.

This avoidance of the subjective dimension has its own drawbacks, two of which may be pointed out here. In the first place, the narrative in important emotional climaxes looks highly unconvincing. Blanchard, in his book *Fielding,* refers to Coleridge's dissatisfaction with the scene of final reconciliation between Tom and Sophia. Nothing could be 'more forced and unnatural'; says Coleridge, 'the language is without vivacity or spirit, the whole matter is incongruous, and totally devoid of psychological truth'. This is merely a stock comic scene having a certain comic life in it but only at the expense of the reality of emotions involved. Similarly, when the hero is expelled from Allworthy's house, we are told that '......he presently fell into the violent agonies, tearing his hair from his head 'and using most other actions which generally accompany fits of madness, rage and despair'; and later that he read Sophia's parting letter 'a hundred times over, and kissed it a hundred times as often' (VI 12) 'Fielding's use of these hackneyed hyperboles to vouch for the intensity of the emotions of his characters underlines the price that he pays for his comic approach: it denies him a convincing and continuous access to the inner life of his characters, so that whenever he has to exhibit their emotional life, he can only do it externally by making them have exaggerated physical reactions.'

The second drawback of this external approach is that it allows the characters very limited possibilities of psychological development. 'Tom Jones's character, for example, exhibits some development, but it is of a very general kind. Tom's early imprudences, his youthful lack of worldly wisdom, and his healthy animality, for example, lead to his disgrace, his expulsion from the Allworthy household, his subsequent difficulties on the road and in London, and his apparently irrecoverable loss of Sophia's love. At the same time, his good qualities, his courage, honour and benevolence, all of which have been glimpsed at the beginning, eventually combine to extricate him from the nadir of his misfortunes, and restore him to the love and respect of those who surround him. But although different qualities come to the fore at different times, they have all been present from the beginning, and we have not been taken close enough to Tom's mind to be able to do anything but take on trust Fielding's implication, which is that his hero will be able to control his weaknesses by the wisdom he has learned of experience.'

But this external approach to character does not imply a deficient understanding of human nature, or as Dr. F.R. Leavis suggests, a 'simple' attitude to it. Fielding's characters are sufficiently alive and convincing. His irony and his comic purpose do produce an effect of distancing between the readers and the—characters and the readers are not allowed either to take an inside view of or to be intimate participants in their feelings. But they are taken close enough (and kept far enough) to be dispassionate observers and impartial judges of their conduct.

Q. 12. "To read *Tom Jones* is a maturing experience; it gives balancing insight into human nature, tolerance for its weaknesses and a larger gratitude for its strength." Do you agree with this ? Give reasons.

Illustrate, by discussing various characters, how Fielding has presented a very authentic picture of human nature, how his characters are neither paragons of virtue nor monsters of vice but real human beings compounded of both good and bad elements and capable of having *happened.* Participation in the various involvements of these characters promotes one's understanding of life and hence is a maturing experience.

Fielding tries to put general human virtues and vices in a proper perspective. His philosophy of life is a very healthy and sound philosophy. He suggests that a person should be tolerant of the weaknesses in others since he is himself guilty of a few and should appreciate others' virtues as he deserves appreciation for his own. Tom's innate goodness of heart and courage deserve applause while his moral lapses, being so very common, should be viewed with tolerance. Illustrate this point by giving more examples.

Read the chapter on Fielding's concept of morality in *Tom Jones* and refer to Q. 3.

Q. 13. "The fact that Fielding's characters do not have a convincing inner life means that their possibilities of psychological development are very limited". Discuss illustrating your answer from *Tom Jones*.

The remark comes from Ian Watt's *The Rise of the Novel.*

One of the major drawbacks of Fielding's external approach to characters is to limit the possibility of their psychological development. Read Q. 11, para 4 to illustrate how Tom's character is not psychologically developed. Illustrate the same point by discussing Squire Allworthy's character whose change in heart appears as unconvincing as his earlier rigidity. The same drawback is in evidence in the final reconciliation scene between Tom and Sophia, whose acquiscence to marriage is not properly prepared for.

Next explain why Fielding had to exclude this psychological development. Refer to Q. 11, para 2.

Tom Jones being a novel of manners, the characters are mostly typed. Fielding wanted to paint the species, not an individual. Characters of manners do not easily lend themselves for detailed psychological analysis. Fielding, quite early in the novel, lays down the essential qualities of a character and the rest of the narrative merely manifests them.

Conclude with the remark that it would be a mistake to consider Fielding an inferior or a second-rate novelist merely because his characters do not develop psychologically. Justify your point by discussing briefly the positive qualities of Fielding's art of characterisation.

Q. 14. Discuss Fielding's description of the novel as 'a comic epic in prose'. How far is this description applicable to Tom Jones ?

For answer, see the chapter '*Tom Jones* as a comic epic in prose'.

Q. 15. "Fielding's realism was not based on rancour or hatred." Examine *Tom Jones* in the light of this remark.

For answer, refer to the chapter on Realism in *Tom Jones.*

Q. 16. Write a brief note on the part played by Sophia's muff in *Tom Jones.*

Sophia's muff is one of the most entertaining devices in *Tom Jones.* It is used as a vital link in a series of widening actions. as a means of clarifying relationships and to assist in characterisation. It is one of those unifying devices that emphasise how conscious and careful Fielding was in the development of his novel.

Since, in the beginning, the muff represents physical attraction between Tom and Sophia, it is not introduced into the story until the two are fairly grown up. And then it is introduced very casually with no hint of its later importance. Sophia's maid, Mrs. Honour reports to her how passionately Tom has kissed it giving her (and the reader) the first hint of Tom's love for her. Next she reports to Tom how the muff has become a prize possession of Sophia and how she kisses it when nobody is looking at her. Thus both Tom and Sophia make the muff a substitutional device which receives their affection.

Next we find the muff involved in a very important scene. One evening, Tom and Squire Western are listening together to Sophia at the harpsichord. As she plays one of her father's favourite tunes, the muff falls over her fingers and puts her out. The disconcerted Squire snatches the muff from her and throws it into the fire. Sophia instantly starts up and recovers it from the flames with utmost eagerness. This clearly shows the intensity of love that now exists between the two. But symbolically it represents much more than this. The muff represents Tom's love for her and her love for Tom. It disturbs her performance at the keyboard and Squire Western throws it into the fire. But she retrieves it even at her own risk. The incident clearly suggests that Tom and Sophia's love for each other is going to be rejected by Squire Western and that Sophia is determined to persist in her love of Tom even if she has to defy the parental authority.

When Tom is expelled from the Allworthy estate, the muff becomes Sophia's substitute for Tom's person, for she weeps over the muff and over Tom's letter to her and keeps the two with her in her bed. When she rejects the proposal of her marriage with Blifil, she again seeks consolation in the muff, which now acts as a reminder of where her true affections lie.

The next appearances of this muff are set at the inn at Upton. Here the muff is again directly instrumental in the action altering the plans of both Tom and Sophia and pressing the plot along. And significantly, the muff also shifts from Sophia's possession into Tom's. When Sophia departs from Upton leaving the muff in Tom's empty bed, it becomes the means by which Tom learns that Sophia has been seeking him and that she is aware of his defection with another woman. He rushes to the kitchen of the inn with the muff in his hand to make enquiries, about how it came to his bed. There he meets Squire Western who, seeing the muff in his hand, immediately suspects that he has stolen it. Tom is held guilty of stealing the muff and a delightful parody of law procedures is enacted.

After this, just as Sophia had earlier made the muff a substitute for Tom's person, now Tom makes it his bedfellow. When Arabella Hunt makes a marriage proposal to Tom, he rejects it, takes out the muff and kisses it several times. Earlier Sophia had rejected Blifil and turned to the muff. Now it is for Tom to turn to it as a reminder of his love for Sophia. The muff is finally dropped from the story when Tom gets Sophia in person.

Thus it is clear that Fielding has made a very significant use of this small piece of dress. Maurice Johnson in *Fielding's Art of Fiction* comments, 'Through the muff Fielding has amusingly drawn attention to states of mind and emotion which, though unformulated and uttered by the characters, impel them into important action or cause them to reject action, thus delineating the characters afresh while drawing the plot into new directions and enforcing the author's thought.'

Q. 17. Is *Tom Jones* a picaresque novel ? Substantiate your answer.

For answer, refer to the chapter '*Tom Jones*' *as a Picaresque Novel.*

Q. 18. Evaluate Henry Fielding's contribution to the development of the novel in England.

For answer, refer to the chapter *Fielding's Contribution to the Development of the English Novel.*

Q. 19. Discuss the statement that *Tom Jones* is the first English novel written to conform to a theory of fiction.

For answer, refer to the chapter '*Tom Jones*' *as a Comic Epic in Prose.*

Q. 20. Examine with reference to *Tom Jones*, Fielding's claim to be regarded as the 'founder of a new province of writing'.

For answer, refer to the chapter '*Tom Jones*' *as a Comic Epic in Prose.*

Q. 21. What do you think Fielding's actual purpose was in writing the chapters that preface each of his eighteen books in *Tom Jones* ? How does this purpose agree with or deviate from his stated purpose ?

Fielding referred to his novel as an epic on account of the very high notions he had of the purpose of the novel. He never believed a novel to be merely a source of entertainment for him. It was a serious form of literature imbued with as serious moral purpose as an epic. Fielding attempted to profoundly influence human thought and behaviour through the medium of the novel. In *Tom Jones* his purpose was to contrast the loveliness of virtue with the ugliness of vice. He emphasises the need of directing one's good intentions intelligently and advocates the pursuit of virtue and avoidance of vice—a very solemn purpose indeed !

Fielding begins each of the books in *Tom Jones* with a prefatory essay which seemingly has no connection with the novel itself. However, he took great pains in writing them. He observes:

> "I can with less pains write one of the books of the history than the prefatory chapter to each of them."

In each of these prefatory chapters he has expressed his ideas on art, literature and life itself.

Fielding says that as a 'bill of fare' is provided to the customers so as to acquaint them with what to expect, similarly an author ought to provide the readers with a general 'bill of fare' to the entire work. Fielding himself gives his readers particular bills to every course which he serves in his volumes. However, in the prefatory chapter to Book one, he broadly classifies his subject as human nature.

The Subject of the Novel: Human Nature

Fielding clearly states that the subject he is dealing with is human nature. He presents both, the ideal and its corruption at the hands of vanity and hypocrisy. Fielding was no less a moralist than Richardson, although his concept of morality was altogether different. He endows Tom, his hero, with a virtuous heart and a natural tendency to benevolence, but at the same time makes him succumb to the enticing viles of the likes of Mrs. Waters, Molly, Mrs. Fitzpatrick and Lady Bellaston.

In the context of his novel, Fielding would like to be judged by the standards of truth. He would like his readers to appeal to their own knowledge and experience of human nature in order to commend or censure his creation.

Dorothy Van Ghent says, "human nature is a balanced mixture of instinctive drives and feelings and intellectual predilections; it is the human tendency to pervert instinct by intellection; it may be altogether bad (as in Master Blifil); it may be altogether good (as in Squire Allworthy)". Some of the views presented by Fielding in his prefatory chapters are as follows:

On Critics:

Fielding draws a clear distinction between a true critic such as Horace or Aristotle and the slanderer or false critic. He is bitter towards indiscreet condemnation by critics whom he calls men of shallow genius who mistake mere form for substance. **John Unsworth** says that critics "who focus on the chaos of the 'Parts' tend to see the comparison as ironic; those, who stand back to admire the 'whole tend to take it at face value.' Fielding believes that every work of art follows its own particular laws for its organic growth and it is imprudent to lay down any dogmatic laws. Fielding also condemns the use of defamatory terms used by false critics who recklessly 'murder', a work of art, rather than giving an accurate judgement.

On Love:

Fielding's concept of love is more tolerant than that of any other Puritan moralist. He associated virtue with goodness and benevolence of heart and not the forced suppression of instinct at the behest of public opinion. Fielding is exasperated at the misconceptions prevalent about love. According to him, love is a kind and generous disposition which gratifies itself by contributing to the happiness of others. This love, when it operates towards one of opposite sex is not mere hunger, though it includes within it that hunger, which heightens the delights of love. Fielding's views were very modern as *John Unsworth* echoes him by saying that, "ideally 'human nature' is one to which all should aspire—a homogeneous configuration of instinct and intelligence—not a suppression of one by the other, but a happy collaboration of the two." These views reinstate the theme of exercising discretion in love, which Tom learns by the end of the novel.

On Human Weaknesses:

Fielding's understanding of human nature is far deeper than what he is credited with. He believes that a person occasionally guilty of a natural weakness is not essentially bad. Hence, any indiscriminate condemnation of persons should be avoided. He says: The man of candour and of true understanding is never hasty to condemn. He can censure an imperfection or even a vice, without rage against the guilty party.

Fielding's sincere effort in *Tom Jones* has been to recommend goodness and innocence. He was more tolerant towards the weakness of the flesh than hypocrisy. "Go deeper than words," says he, "and judge deeds; go deeper than deeds and judge intentions which are the immediate expression of the soul. Go deeper than even conscious intentions."

Law of Credibility in the Novel

Fielding advocates three laws for a practising novelist to ensure credibility in his work. The first, being the rule of possibility. Fielding suggests that miracles and supernatural intervention should be avoided. The law of cause and effect should be followed and all that a novelist narrates in the novel should be within the range of human capacity. The second, is the rule of probability. Fielding is not in favour of narrating improbable events as their occurrence is rare in real life. Characters should not be embodiments of only virtue or only vice as rogues may have goodness of heart, and the virtuous may have evil designs within. According to the third rule, Fielding believes that the behaviour of a character should be consistent with his nature. His actions should be possible and probable within the compass of human nature.

Fielding's prefatory chapters also include what may be called the 'qualifications of a novelist'. This talent, says Fielding, comprises genius, learning, conversation and sensibility. Fielding describes the contemporary society in the following words:

In my humble opinion, the characteristic of the present beaumonde is rather folly than vice, and the only epithet it deserves is that of frivolous.

Thus, the prefatory chapters may be regarded as Fielding's commentary on art, literature and life, as such they are of abiding interest for a student of literature. Insofar as he talks of human life, its variety and its follies, Fielding reiterates his purpose of showing by contrast the ugliness of vice and the loveliness of virtue in the characters of Blifil and Sophia respectively.

To realize his moral purpose Fielding had to show how the goodness of Tom had to combat dangers in its hazardous course to maturity and knowledge. Although he succumbs to sexual pleasures at times, nowhere does he indicate a vicious disposition. Fielding asserts that it is man's duty to exercise prudence as Squire Allworthy says "Prudence and circumspection are necessary even to the best of men. They are a guard to virtue without which it can never be safe." The views expressed in the prefatory chapters such as those on love, morality, human weakness and credibility in a novel, are all well illustrated in the course of *Tom Jones* and reinforced throughout the events in the book. Fielding follows the law of cause and effect, without any major improbable or impossible turn of events while narrating the journey of his hero Tom. Tom is portrayed as a lusty, passionate, highly sexed man of a virtuous disposition whose marriage with Sophia at the end of the novel assures the reader that his virility will no longer run to waste, as in the past, but will be contained inside the larger needs of his own virtue, the needs of loyalty, tenderness, affection and healthy perpetuation of the race.

24

Additional Questions for Discussion

1. "The material of the novelist is (*a*) the world of human beings and (*b*) their relations to each other." Examine *Tom Jones* in the light of this remark.
2. "Fielding's greatest achievement is that he took the traditional standard types but because of the vitality of his vision, his characters are bouncingly alive." Comment.
3. "It is his (Fielding's) broad, tolerant nature and his humour which makes his characters so vitally alive." Comment.
4. "*Tom Jones* is a wholesome human book. Fielding quite honestly made his hero fallible that he might make him human." Do you agree with this view ?
5. What narrative devices does Fielding employ to unify the wide variety of characters and incidents in *Tom Jones* and with what success ? Give a reasoned answer.
6. "Fielding's characters, though simple in outline, possess great complexity." Discuss with special reference to *Tom Jones.*
7. "Fielding offers not merely an interesting narrative but a responsible wisdom that plays upon the deeds and characters of the novel." Discuss with special reference to *Tom Jones.*
8. Says Ian Watt about Fielding: "He believed that virtue, far from being the result of the suppression of instinct at the behest of the public opinion, was itself a natural tendency to goodness or benevolence." What goodness do you find in the character of Tom Jones ?
9. "The struggle of Tom Jones and Sophia against Blifil and all that he stands for is at the very centre of the novel (*Tom Jones*)." Discuss.
10. "Tom is human nature as Fielding would have it been, seen against a panorama of the follies, vices and hypocrisies of the world as it is." Consider the aptness of this remark.
11. "*Tom Jones* gives a combined impression of tradition still in living contact with the social fact, and of original comic genius rendering truly what human nature is." Illuminate.
12. "*Tom Jones* then lacks sustained intensity; it does not make the heroic impression and on that account it fails as on epic." Comment.

13. Fielding says that in *Tom Jones* he has portrayed human character in its 'prodigious variety'. Elucidate.

14. "Fielding has that broad tolerant nature, that faculty of observation, that curiosity of life for itself, which usually go to make the creators of characters." Amplify and illustrate.

15. Fielding has the undeniable merit of representing certain aspects of contemporary society with a force and accuracy not ever rivalled by any other writer. Discuss this statement with special reference to *Tom Jones*.

16. What effect is achieved by the introduction of the theme of incest in *Tom Jones* ? Discuss in detail.

17. To what extent is it possible to regard *Tom Jones* as an example of "the ironic novel—a species of novel in which an author consciously sets on the real conduct of every day against the large abstractions of moral values, classical literature, or myth" ?

18. Critically examine the view that "Tom and Sophia are rebels, revolting against the respectably accepted domestic standards of eighteenth-century society."

19. Fielding declared that his purpose in *Tom Jones* was to show how "to make good men wise". To what extent is this borne out by the career of his hero ?

20. "For better, for worse, Fielding determined the course of the English novel for the next hundred years." Discuss *Tom Jones* in the light of this statement.

21. Tom Jones has often been praised for the cleverness of the plot. The plot has also been criticized for dominating the novel and for being too contrived. Is emotional involvement sacrificed to the plot ? Does plotting dominate the book too greatly ? Does the plot seem too contrived ?

22. What is the point of the Man of the Hills' story in the context of the novel ? In terms of plot and theme ? Does this interpolated narrative help heighten the novel or merely slow it down ?

23. Fielding compares the narrator to God, and the novel to his world. Does he portray this world as balanced and ordered or as arbitrary and filled with coincidence ? Explain.

24. In what ways is Tom Jones an allegory ?

25

Chronology of Important Dates

1707	Fielding born at Sharpham Park, near Glastonbury, Somerset.
1709–24	Education at Eton.
1724	Love affair with Sarah and an unsuccessful attempt to abduct her.
1728	A satiric poem *The Masquerade* is published. The first play *Love in Several Masques* is produced. Fielding registers as a student of letters, University of Leyden.
1729	Discontinues studies at Leyden and takes up residence in London.
1730	Fielding's career as a dramatist. His various comedies including *The Author's Farce* (1730), *Rape Upon Rape* (1730), *Tom Thumb* (1730), *The Modern Husband* (1732), *The Miser* (1733), *Don Quixote in England* (1734), *The Historical Register* (1737) produced.
1734	Elopement and marriage with Charlotte Cradock.
1737	The Licensing Act of 1737 is passed.
1740	Richardson's *Pamela* or *Virtue Rewarded* published.
1741	*Shamela,* a parody of *Pamela* brought out.
1742	*Joseph Andrews* published.
1743	*Miscellanies* including *Jonathan Wild* published.
1744	Charlotte Cradock dies.
1745–46	Edits *The True Patriot.*
1747	Marries his housekeeper Mary Daniel. Richardson's *Clarissa* published.
1749	*Tom Jones* published.
1751	*Amelia* published.
1754	Sets out on a voyage to Lisbon. Dies on October 8 in Junqueira near Libson.

Select Bibliography

Biography

1. *Butt, John* : Fielding, "Writers and Their Works," No. 57, 1954.
2. *Cross, Wilbur* : The History of Henry Fielding, 3 vols., 1918.
3. *Dudden, F. Homes* : Henry Fielding: His Life, Works and Times, 2 vols., 1952.

Criticism

4. *Alter, Robert* . Fielding and the Nature of the Novel, 1968.
5. *Baker, E.A.* : "Tom Jones," The History of the English Novel, Volume IV, 1930.
6. *Bettestin, M.C. (Ed.)* : Twentieth Century Interpretations of 'Tom Jones', 1968.
7. *Blanchard, F.T.* : Fielding the Novelist: A Study of the Novelist's Fame and Influence, 1926.
8. *Bowers, Fredson (Ed.)* : The History of Tom Jones, A Foundling (Oxford University Press, 1975).
9. *Comptom, Neil (Ed.)* : A Selection of Critical Essays on Tom Jones' (Case Book Series), 1970.
10. *Crane, R.S.* : "The Plot of Tom Jones," 1950. Reprinted in Twentieth Century Interpretations of Tom Jones'.
11. *Digeon, Aurelion* : The Novels of Fielding, 1952.
12. *Drew, Elizabeth* : "Tom Jones" in The Novel, 1963.
13. *Ehrenpreis, Irvin* : Fielding: Tom Jones, 1964.
14. *Hatfield, Glenn W.* : Henry Fielding and the Language of Irony, 1968.
15. *Hutchcns, Eleanor N.* : " 'Prudence' in Tom Jones: A Study of Connotative Irony," Philological Quarterly XXXIX, 1960.
16. *Irwin, Michael* : Henry Fielding: The Tentative Realist, 1967.
17. *Iser, Wolfgang* : The Act of Reading (1978).

18. *Johnson, Maurice* : Fielding's Art of Fiction, 1961.

19. *Kaul A.N.* : The Action of English Comedy (1970)

20. *Kermode, Frank* : Richardson and Fielding: Cambridge Journal IV, 1950.

21. *Kettle, Arnold* : An Introduction to the English Novel, Vol. I, 1951.

22. *Macallister, Hamilton* : Fielding (Literature in Perspective series), 1967.

23. *McKillop, Alan D.* : "Fielding" in "The Early Masters of English Fiction," 1956.

24. *Murry, John M.* : "In Defence of Fielding" in 'Unprofessional Essays', Reprinted in Twentieth Century Views on Fielding, 1956.

25. *Muller, R.P.C. (Ed.)* : Henry Fielding: Tom Jones (A Penguin edition of the text with a very useful introduction), 1966.

26. *Paulson, Ronald (Ed.)* : Fielding: A Collection of Critical Essays (Twentieth Century Views on Fielding), 1962.

27. *Preston, John* : "Tom Jones and the Pursuit of True Judgment" in ELH XXXIII, 1966.

28. *Rawson, C.J.* : Henry Fielding (Profiles in Literature series), 1968.

29. *Rawson, C.J. (Ed.)* : Henry Fielding (Peguine Critical Anthologies) (a very useful anthology of Fieling criticism from eighteenth century to present day), 1973.

30. *Snow, Malinda* : "The Judgement of Evidence in Tom Jones" (1983).

31. *Thornbury, E.M.* : Henry Fielding's Theory of the Comic Prose Epic, 1931.

32. *Tillyard, E.M.W.* : The Epic Strain in the English Novel, 1958.

33. *Unsworth, John* : Modern Language Quarterly (1987).

34. *Van Ghent, Dorothy* "On Tom Jones" in the English Novel: Form and Function, 1953.

35. *Watt, Ian* : The Rise of the Novel, 1957.

36 *Wright, Andrew* : Henry Fielding: Mask and Feast, 1963.

NOTES

NOTES